Unit 4

Unit 5

Unit 6

McGRAW-HILL READING

Phonics and Phonemic Awareness

Grade 2   Practice Book

McGraw-Hill
School Division
New York   Farmington

Contents

The Sounds of Initial Consonants

Draw a circle around the picture whose name begins with the same sound as the first picture in each row.

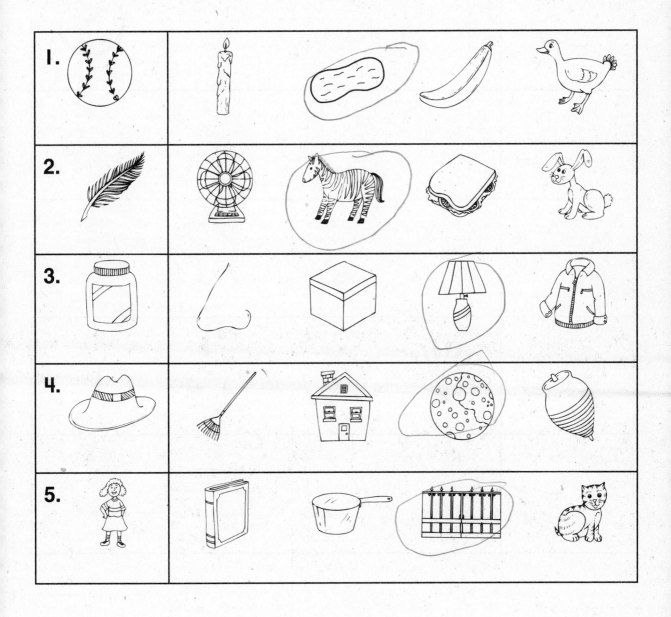

The Sounds of Final Consonants

Draw a circle around the picture whose name ends with the same sound as the first picture in each row.

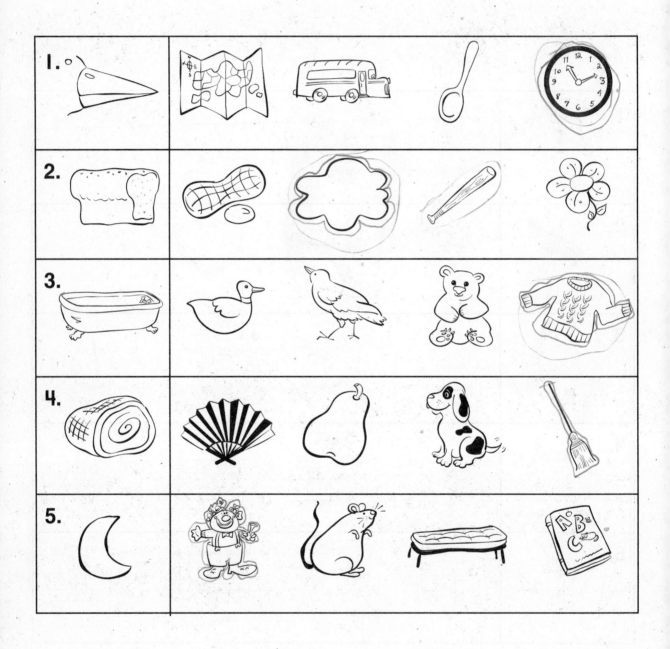

Name _____ Date _____

The Sounds of Initial Consonants

Draw a circle around the picture whose name begins with the same sound as the first picture in each row.

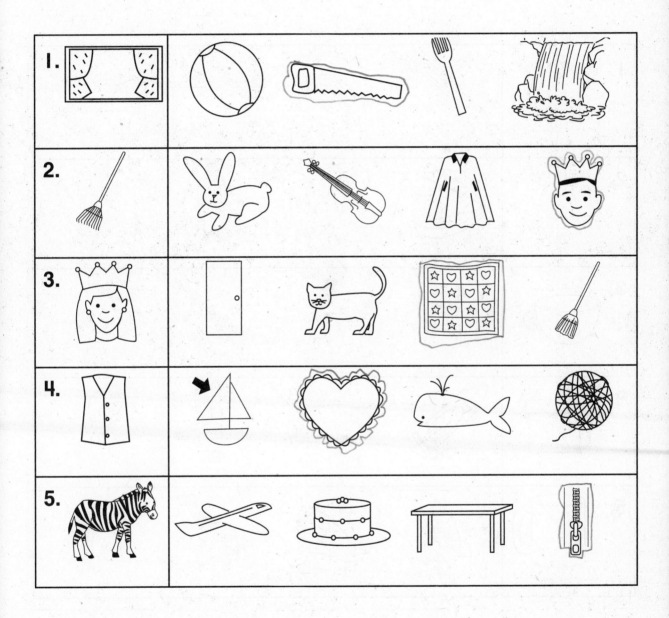

The Sounds of Final Consonants

Draw a circle around the picture whose name ends with the same sound as the first picture in each row.

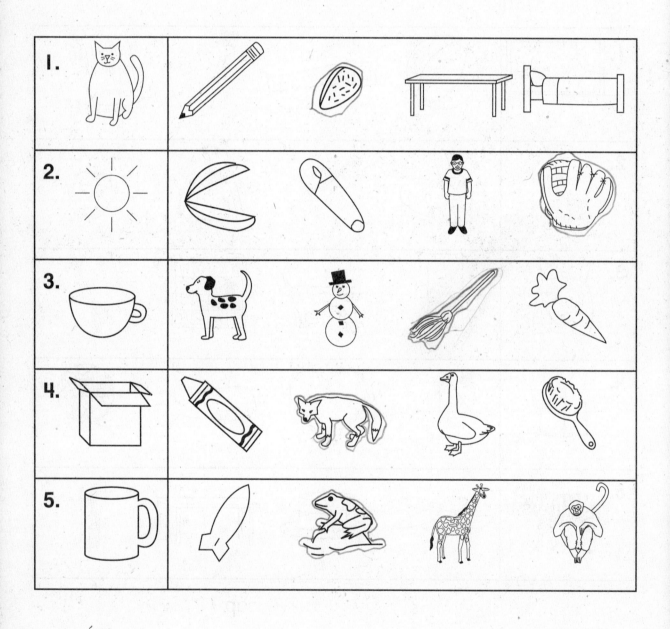

Initial and Final Consonants

Look at the picture. Draw a circle around the correct word to finish the sentence. Then write it on the line.

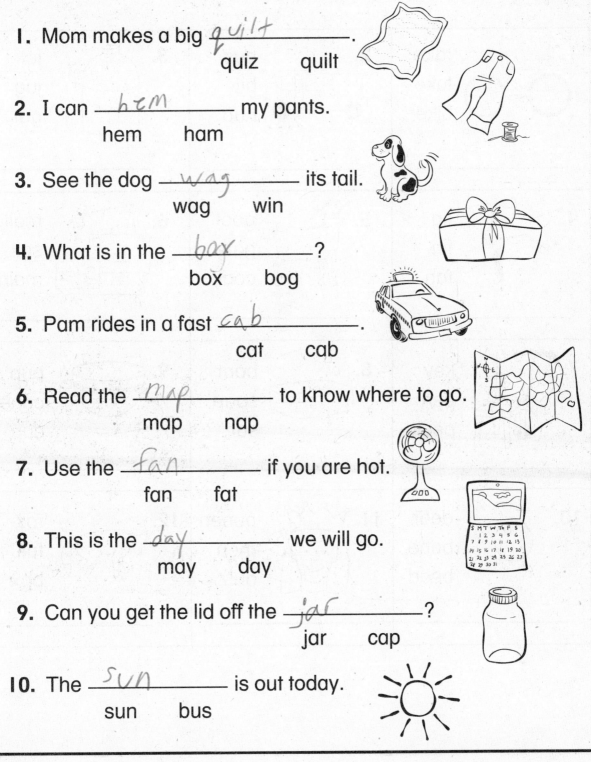

1. Mom makes a big _quilt_ .

        quiz   quilt

2. I can _hem_ my pants.

   hem   ham

3. See the dog _wag_ its tail.

     wag   win

4. What is in the _box_ ?

     box   bog

5. Pam rides in a fast _cab_ .

     cat   cab

6. Read the _map_ to know where to go.

   map   nap

7. Use the _fan_ if you are hot.

   fan   fat

8. This is the _day_ we will go.

   may   day

9. Can you get the lid off the _jar_ ?

     jar   cap

10. The _sun_ is out today.

   sun   bus

Initial and Final Consonants

Draw a circle around the word that names the picture. Then write the word.

1. rake / take / **bike** — _bike_	**2.** **bus** / bit / bug — _bus_	**3.** jet / **jug** / got — _jug_
4. fig / **fin** / fan — _fin_	**5.** **goat** / gate / coal — _goate_	**6.** **mail** / sail / main — _mail_
7. key / pen / **peek** — _peek_	**8.** boat / **soap** / sat — _soap_	**9.** pup / cone / **cup** — _cup_
10. dear / **bone** / bead — _bone_	**11.** **queen** / men / quiz — _queen_	**12.** **fox** / full / box — _fox_

Name _____ Date _____

Initial and Final Consonants

Draw a circle around the word to finish the sentence. Then write the word on the line.

1. The ___*hen*___ sets on her nest.
   men   hen

2. ___*Let*___ me see your new pet.
   Let   Wet

3. The little _____ likes to eat a lot of food.
   pig   rig

4. _____ little cats are for sale.
   Pen   Ten

5. We see big cats at the _____.
   zoo   fix

6. I take my cat to the _____.
   tug   vet

7. Jill has a red _____.
   cap   cut

8. How many more make _____?
   six   sit

9. We like to _____ rope together.
   lump   jump

10. Then we play ball with a _____.
    net   set

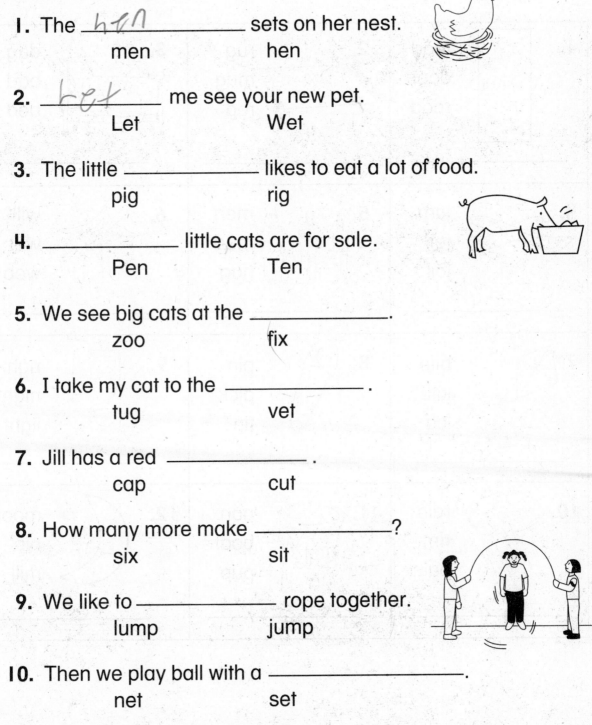

Initial and Final Consonants

Draw a circle around the word that names the picture. Then write the word.

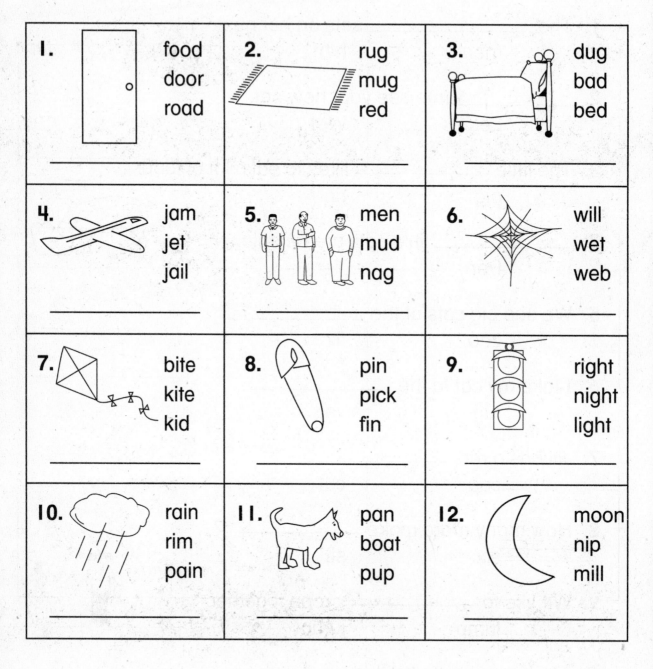

1. food door road	**2.** rug mug red	**3.** dug bad bed
4. jam jet jail	**5.** men mud nag	**6.** will wet web
7. bite kite kid	**8.** pin pick fin	**9.** right night light
10. rain rim pain	**11.** pan boat pup	**12.** moon nip mill

The Sounds of Blends

Draw a circle around the picture whose name begins with the same sounds as the first picture in each row.

The Sounds of Blends

Name the pictures in each row. Put an X on the picture that does not begin with the same sounds as the others.

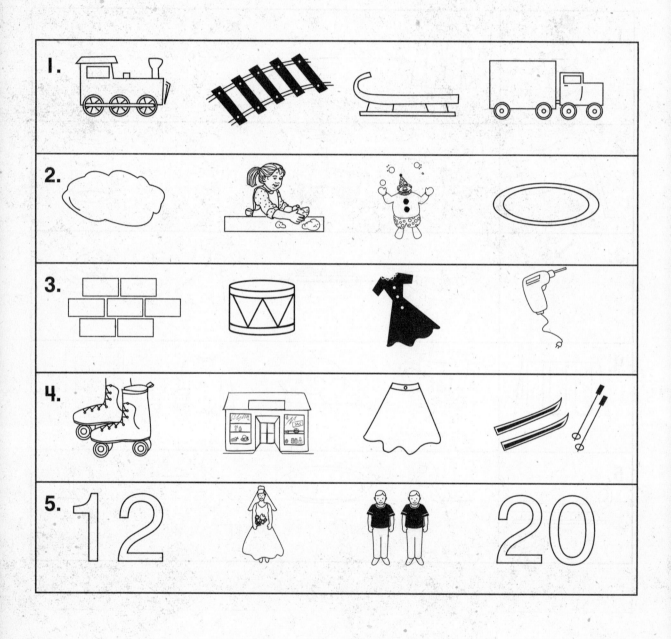

The Sounds of Blends

Name the pictures in each row. Draw a circle around the pictures whose names begin with the same sounds.

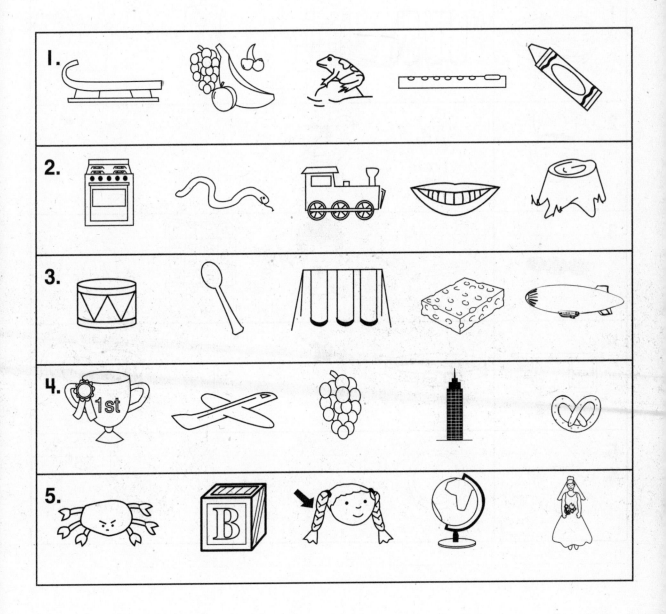

The Sounds of Final Blends

Draw a line under the picture whose name ends with the same sounds as the first picture in each row.

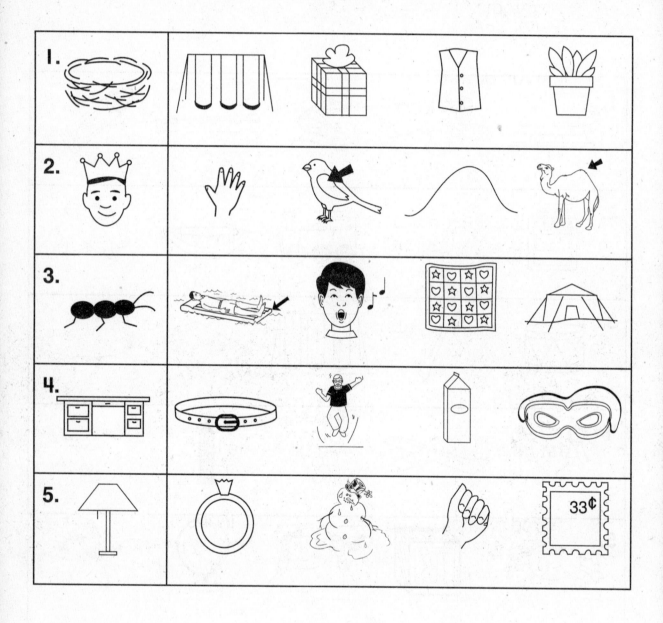

Blends

Look at the picture. Draw a circle around the correct word to finish the sentence. Then write the word on the line.

1. We can make a _____ together.

   snowman   smoke

2. Pam ran down the _____ fast.

   hint   hill

3. Dad will mow the _____ soon.

   grass   glass

4. Tim plays the _____ in the band.

   flute   frost

5. The _____ ate the chips.

   gruff   gull

6. I wear a _____ when I paint.

   stand   smock

7. Try not to _____ on the ice.

   slip   spill

8. I found a small _____ in the pool.

   flog   frog

9. I have _____ pens.

   twelve   trays

10. _____ when you see this.

   Stop   Play

Blends

Name the pictures. Then choose the correct word from the word box. Write the word.

vest	stamp	smoke	flag	dress	plant
well	milk	tusk	twelve	king	clap

1.

_____

2.

_____

3.

_____

4.

_____

5.

_____

6.

_____

7.

_____

8.

_____

9.

_____

10.

_____

11.

_____

12.

_____

Blends

Look at the picture. Draw a circle around the correct word to finish the sentence. Write it on the line.

1. The stars ——————————— in the night sky.

slow   glow

2. The little bird sings on the tree ———————————.

branch   flinch

3. My mom can ——————————— a truck.

drive   twine

4. The bell makes a loud ———————————.

bring   clang

5. One pig made a house from ———————————.

twigs   tricks

6. The king likes to wear his ———————————.

clown   crown

7. Will you ——————————— ball with us?

play   class

8. Throw this in the ——————————— can.

trash   crash

9. Plants ——————————— in the bright sun.

snow   grow

10. I would like to ride in a ———————————.

blimp   tramp

Name_____ Date_____

Blends

Name the pictures. Then choose the correct word from the word box. Write the word.

sniff	cast	slip	doll	clam	brush
sleep	nest	plum	cuff	spool	left

1. _____

2. _____

3. _____

4. _____

5. _____

6. _____

7. _____

8. _____

9. _____

10. _____

11. _____

12. _____

The Sounds of Digraphs

Draw a circle around the picture whose name begins with the same sound as the first picture in each row.

Name _____ Date _____

The Sounds of Digraphs

Draw a circle around the picture whose name ends with the same sound as the first picture.

The Sounds of Blends

Name the pictures in each row. Draw a circle around the pictures whose names begin with the same sounds.

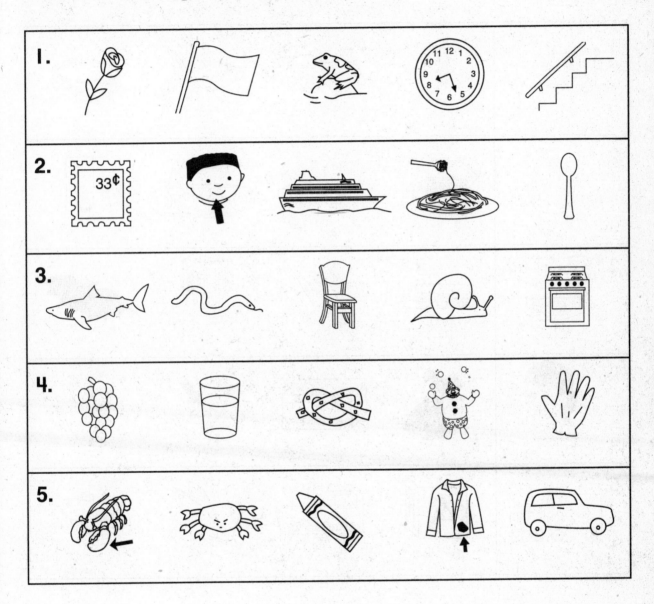

The Sounds of Final Blends and Digraphs

Draw a line under the picture that ends with the same sound as the first picture in each row.

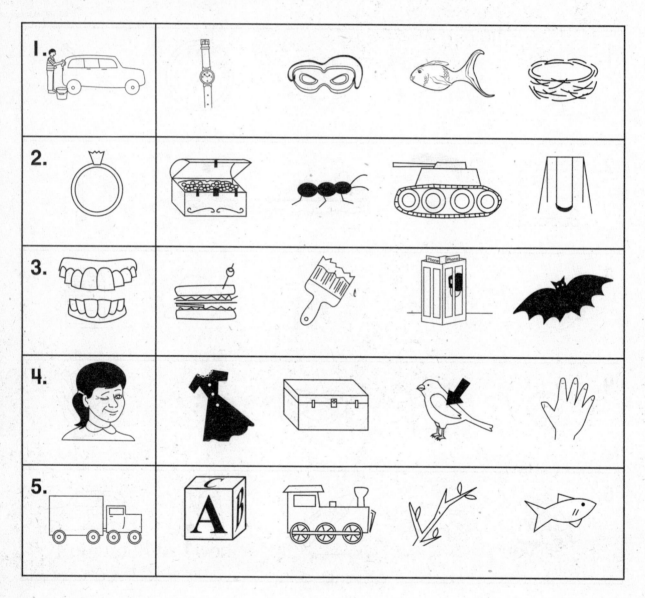

Grade 2

Digraphs

Draw a circle around the word to finish each sentence. Then write it on the line.

1. We will have _____ at noon.

   luck   lunch

2. This rose is _____ and pretty.

   fresh   faith

3. Can you come to the shop _____ me?

   with   will

4. Then we can play _____.

   shed   chess

5. My bike needs a new _____.

   wheel   think

6. The tire is too _____.

   thin   chimp

7. _____ you for the help you gave me.

   Thank   Thing

8. Will you _____ to see how fast I can run?

   shape   check

9. Where is that _____ going to stop?

   truck   them

10. I _____ it would stop at my house.

   dish   wish

Blends and Digraphs

Draw a circle around the word that names the picture. Then write the word.

1. chain reach shine _____	**2.** queen wheel shelf _____	**3.** chick shake chip _____
4. skull trunk skunk _____	**5.** fish fast risk _____	**6.** brake brush branch _____
7. track thin chin _____	**8.** shack steal shell _____	**9.** belt bath back _____
10. whale shale chest _____	**11.** king ranch bank _____	**12.** block brush blink _____

Blends and Digraphs

Write the correct word on the line.

1. My cat is ————————————— and white.

             gray   pray

2. My cold makes me ————————————.

             when   sneeze

3. The train runs on the ————————————.

             track   trunk

4. Bill will ————————————— the toys in a big bag.

          sting   stuff

5. I will paint the sky a ————————————— of blue.

             chain   shade

6. The paint is too ————————————.

             thick   thank

7. Dad and Bill will fish in the ————————————.

             creek   cheek

8. Mom likes to skate at the ————————————.

             rake   rink

9. She does not ————————————— on the ice.

          slick   slip

10. The clock will ————————————— when
    it is time to eat.

          chime   whine

Blends and Digraphs

Draw a circle around the word that names the picture. Then write the word.

1. thick trick trunk _____	**2.** bride prize click _____	**3.** boot push booth _____
4. flag frog crank _____	**5.** trick tray that _____	**6.** chink shine chin _____
7. thing swing wick _____	**8.** duck drum stuck _____	**9.** show snow blow _____
10. raft rash risk _____	**11.** blink bench belt _____	**12.** press plus dress _____

Grade 2

The Sounds of Short Vowels

Draw a circle around the picture whose name has the same vowel sound as the first picture in each row.

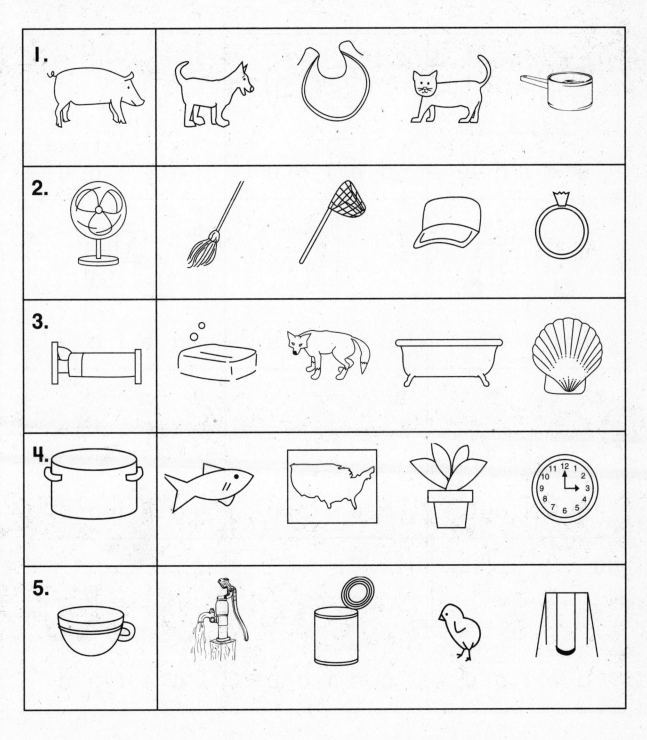

Short Vowels

Name each picture. Draw a circle around the letter that stands for the short vowel sound.

1. a e i o u	2. a e i o u	3. a e i o u
4. a e i o u	5. a e i o u	6. a e i o u
7. a e i o u	8. a e i o u	9. a e i o u
10. a e i o u	11. a e i o u	12. a e i o u

Short Vowels

Draw a circle around each word that has the same vowel sound as the name of the picture.

1.	bed sled feet check	2.	ship twin bush click	3.	hut drip sun chum
4.	flat flop cot smock	5.	chat chick bath shack	6.	vase snack smash plan
7.	gruff moon plum chug	8.	shell chess drink step	9.	quit whip slim slice
10.	stop strip blot rock	11.	bang branch head sad	12.	swim swam quilt grill

Name _____ Date _____

Short Vowels

Draw a circle around the correct word to finish the sentence. Then write it on the line.

1. Joy and Bill are putting up a _____.

      tent   tank

2. A _____ is in the tree.

  net   nest

3. Bill holds the rope so it does not _____.

  skip   slip

4. Joy _____ on her flashlight.

  flicked   rigged

5. Brad is at the food _____.

  strap   shack

6. Brad can see the _____ on the shore.

  gulls   gums

7. He can see how they flap their _____.

  things   wings

8. Now Brad will go to the _____ to see the ships.

  stock   dock

The Sounds of Long Vowels

Draw a circle around the picture whose name has the same vowel sound as the first picture in each row.

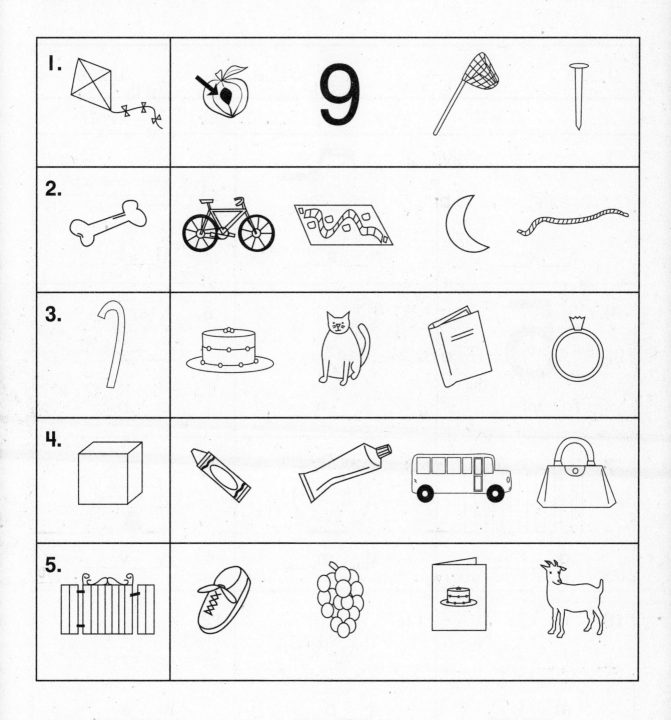

Name_____ Date_____

Long Vowels

Name each picture. Find the long vowel sound letters in the box.
Write the letters on the lines.

a __ e	i __ e	o __ e	u __ e

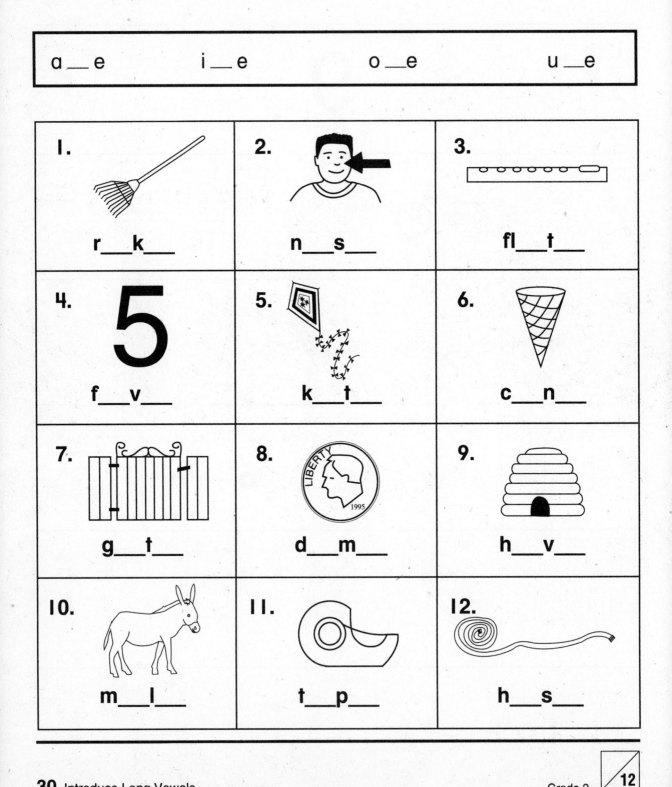

1. r __ __ k __ __

2. n __ __ s __ __

3. fl __ t __

4. f __ __ v __ __

5. k __ __ t __ __

6. c __ n __ __

7. g __ t __ __

8. d __ __ m __ __

9. h __ v __ __

10. m __ __ l __ __

11. t __ p __

12. h __ __ s __ __

Long Vowels

Draw a line from the riddle to the answer. Draw a circle around the letters that make the long vowel sound in the answer.

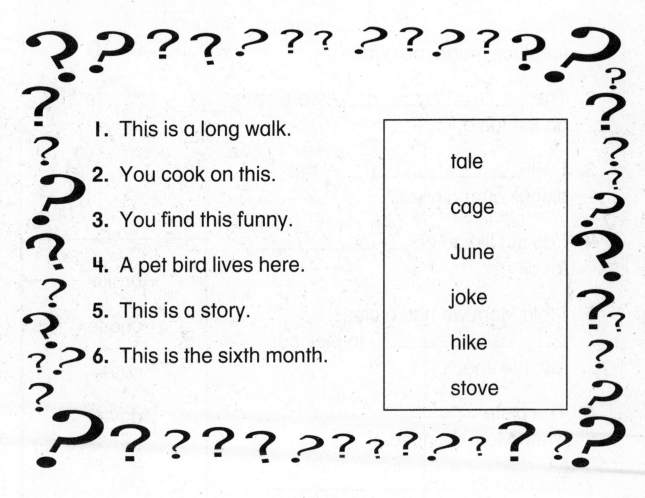

1. This is a long walk.

2. You cook on this.

3. You find this funny.

4. A pet bird lives here.

5. This is a story.

6. This is the sixth month.

tale

cage

June

joke

hike

stove

Name _____ Date _____

Long Vowels

Find the word in the box that will finish each sentence. Write it on the line.

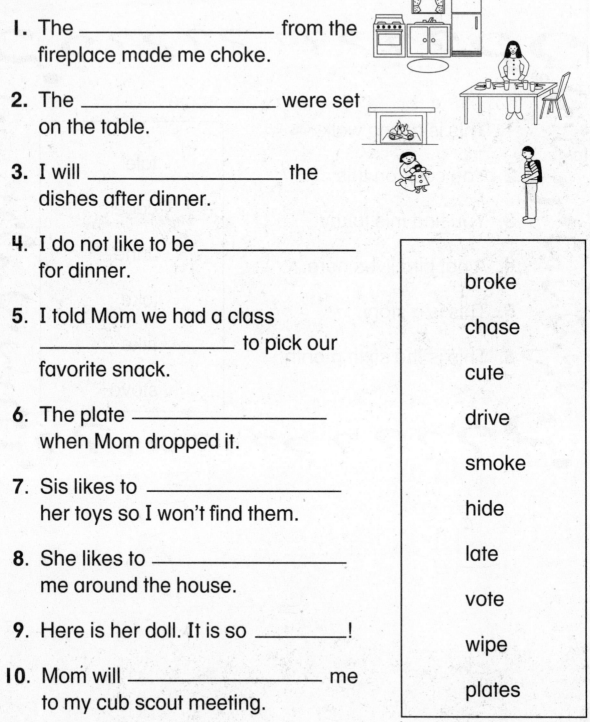

1. The _____ from the fireplace made me choke.

2. The _____ were set on the table.

3. I will _____ the dishes after dinner.

4. I do not like to be _____ for dinner.

5. I told Mom we had a class _____ to pick our favorite snack.

6. The plate _____ when Mom dropped it.

7. Sis likes to _____ her toys so I won't find them.

8. She likes to _____ me around the house.

9. Here is her doll. It is so _____!

10. Mom will _____ me to my cub scout meeting.

broke

chase

cute

drive

smoke

hide

late

vote

wipe

plates

The Sounds of Long *a* and Long *e*

Find the following objects in the picture.

tree	train	pail	eat	tail
tray	feet	wheat	wheels	read

Draw a circle around the pictures whose names have the **long a** sound. Mark an **X** on the pictures whose names have the **long e** sound.

Name_____ Date_____

Long *a* and Long *e*

Name each picture. Draw a circle around the letters that stand for the long vowel sound.

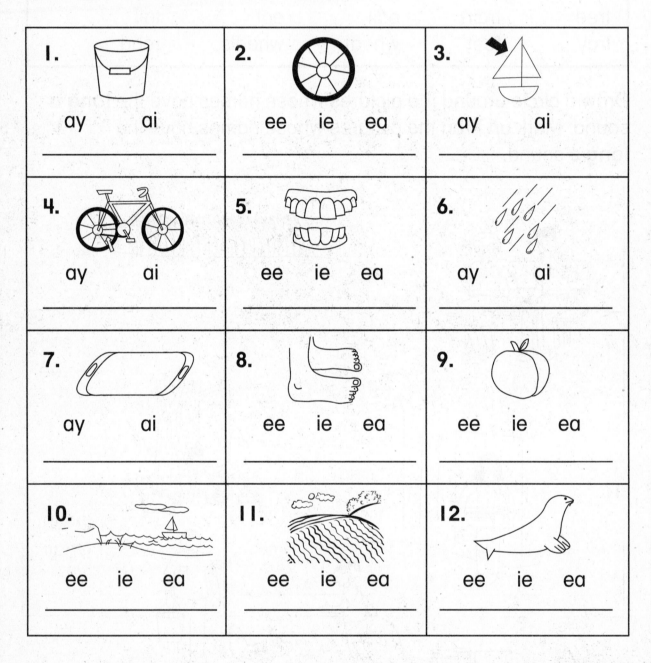

1. ay   ai
_____

2. ee   ie   ea
_____

3. ay   ai
_____

4. ay   ai
_____

5. ee   ie   ea
_____

6. ay   ai
_____

7. ay   ai
_____

8. ee   ie   ea
_____

9. ee   ie   ea
_____

10. ee   ie   ea
_____

11. ee   ie   ea
_____

12. ee   ie   ea
_____

Long *a* and Long *e*

Draw a circle around the name of each picture.

1. fail field fume	2. teeth tail take	3. net nice nail
4. clay claim close	5. lean leaf leap	6. beat beam bee
7. braid beak brake	8. cheek cane chain	9. tree three the
10. hay hail hee	11. brain tail train	12. nails stain snail

Long *a* and Long *e*

Draw a circle around the correct word to finish the sentence. Then write it on the line.

1. It is a pretty fall _____.

              dig   day

2. It is a good day to _____ a walk.

             take   tick

3. Mrs. Green went to the store to buy some _____.

             meal   meat

4. She also has some _____ in her cart.

             beets   beaks

5. Mr. and Mrs. Green will cook a good _____ .

             mail   meal

6. Rod and Ramon like to _____ at the pond.

             plain   play

7. Ramon _____ his leg last week.

             sprained   sprayed

8. He is not in any _____ now.

             pain   peek

9. The _____ fell off!

             same   sail

10. It is time to stop and have something to _____.

             eat   each

Name _____ Date _____

The Sounds of Long *i* and Long *o*

Draw a circle around the picture whose name has the same long vowel as the first picture in each row.

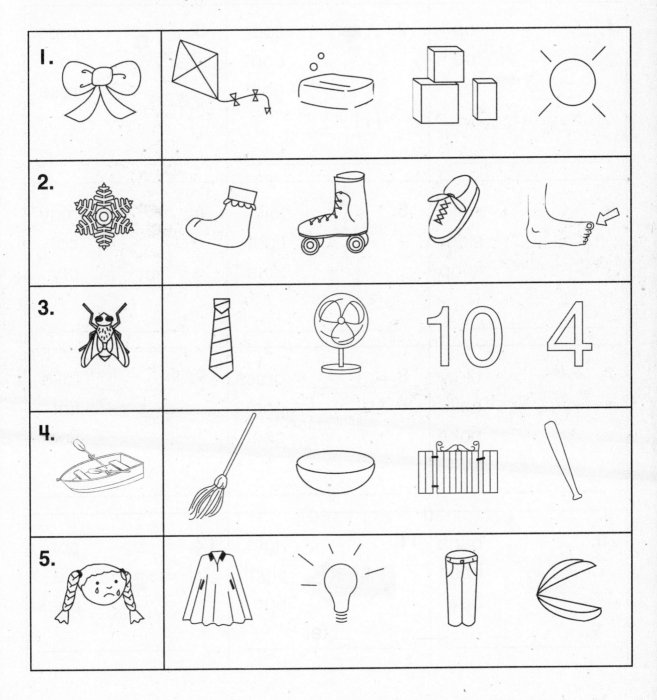

Long *i* and Long *o*

Draw a circle around the name of each picture.

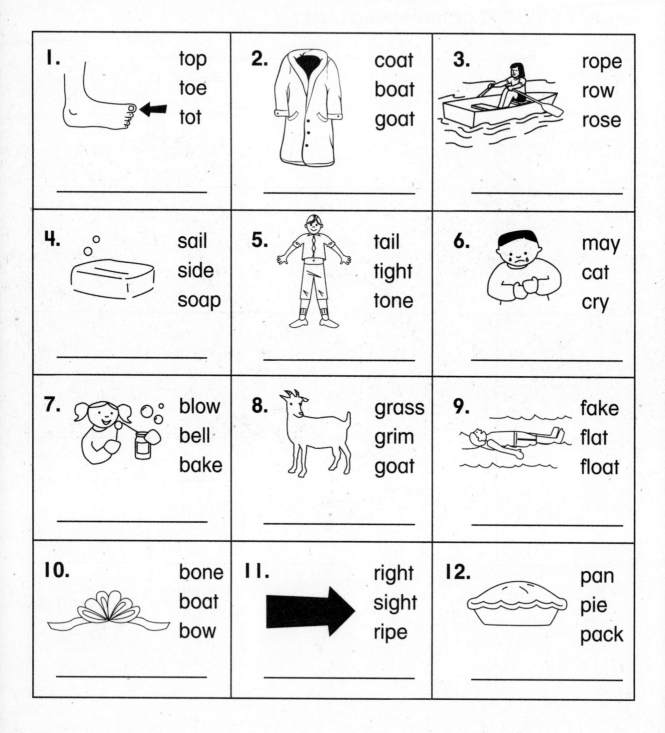

1. top / toe / tot

2. coat / boat / goat

3. rope / row / rose

4. sail / side / soap

5. tail / tight / tone

6. may / cat / cry

7. blow / bell / bake

8. grass / grim / goat

9. fake / flat / float

10. bone / boat / bow

11. right / sight / ripe

12. pan / pie / pack

Long *i* and Long *o*

Draw a line to the word that answers each riddle. Then draw a circle around the letters in the word that stand for the long vowel sound.

1. If you don't turn left, you turn this way.

2. This is the time when it is dark.

3. This is part of a foot.

4. You look out of this.

5. This is where you see the stars.

6. You may do this when you are sad.

7. This is a small bug.

8. It keeps you warm.

9. You use a sled in this.

10. You eat this.

coat

sky

fly

snow

pie

right

night

toe

window

cry

Name _____ Date _____

Long *i* and Long *o*

Find the word in the box that will finish each sentence. Write it on the line.

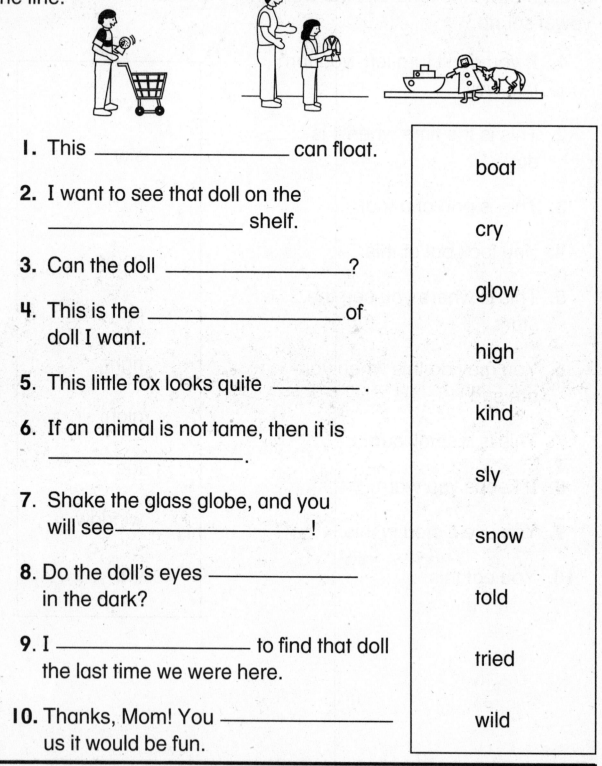

1. This _____ can float.

2. I want to see that doll on the _____ shelf.

3. Can the doll _____?

4. This is the _____ of doll I want.

5. This little fox looks quite _____.

6. If an animal is not tame, then it is _____.

7. Shake the glass globe, and you will see _____!

8. Do the doll's eyes _____ in the dark?

9. I _____ to find that doll the last time we were here.

10. Thanks, Mom! You _____ us it would be fun.

boat
cry
glow
high
kind
sly
snow
told
tried
wild

Review Short Vowels and Long Vowels

Draw a circle around the word that answers each riddle.

1. It is on your face.
   shin   chin   chat

2. A dog likes this.
   bone   bake   brake

3. When you add, you get this.
   sun   sum   stamp

4. You can have fun on this.
   slip   small   slide

5. This is a small box.
   cape   cube   cure

6. You can do this to grass.
   mop   mow   men

7. This is the way to cook a cake.
   brush   bean   bake

8. When you jump on one foot, you do this.
   hope   hop   hip

9. You write this.
   note   nose   nut

10. You fly in this.
    plane   plan   bike

Review Short Vowels and Long Vowels

Name each picture. Find its name in the word box. Then write the word in the puzzle.

blow	bride	bus	crib	cry	hose	leaf	pail
pants	pen	pot	rain	toe	tray	wheel	

Across

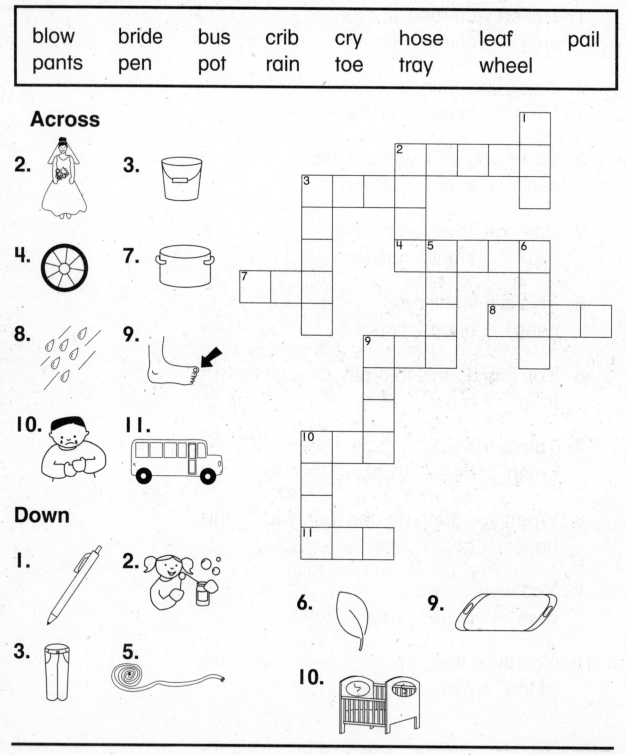

2.

3.

4.

7.

8.

9.

10.

11.

Down

1.

2.

3.

5.

6.

9.

10.

Review Short Vowels and Long Vowels

Add the missing letter or letters to each word.

1. It is a nice spr———ng day.   e   i   u

2. I have lots of s———ds to plant.   ee   ai   a

3. I use a h——— for digging.   ai   oe   ay

4. I sh——— Mom what I planted.   ee   ai   ow

5. She likes the red b———ts.   ee   ai   e

6. These plants will get a lot of sunl———t.   ai   ee   igh

7. I will just spr——— the plants with water.   y   ee   ay

8. It is going to r———n tonight.   a   ai   oa

9. OOPS! My f———t are getting wet.   ee   ai   i

10. I must go in and put dr——— socks on.   oe   y   ay

Review Short Vowels and Long Vowels

Find the word that means the opposite. Write it on the line.

dry	float	high	hot	mean	night
run	shade	stand	stay	thin	yes

1. wet _____

2. day _____

3. sink _____

4. thick _____

5. cold _____

6. walk _____

7. sun _____

8. sit _____

9. low _____

10. go _____

11. kind _____

12. no _____

The man told Dad, "Those are two nice kids you've got!" Dad just smiled and waved good-bye.

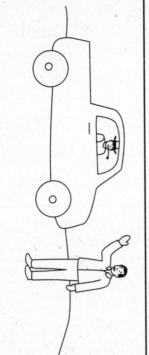

One day, a man came by to see Dad and me.

He said, "I like goat cheese and milk. I'll pay three times ten for your goat."

Fold the right side back on the long center line. Then fold the top half under the bottom half on the short center line. Cut open the tops of the pages.

Meet My Goat, Lucky

This little book belongs to

_____

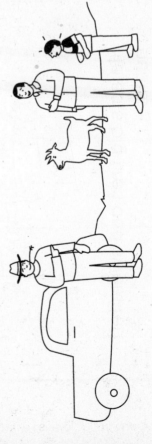

"No way! No Sale! Not today or ever!"
I said. "Lucky is my pet."

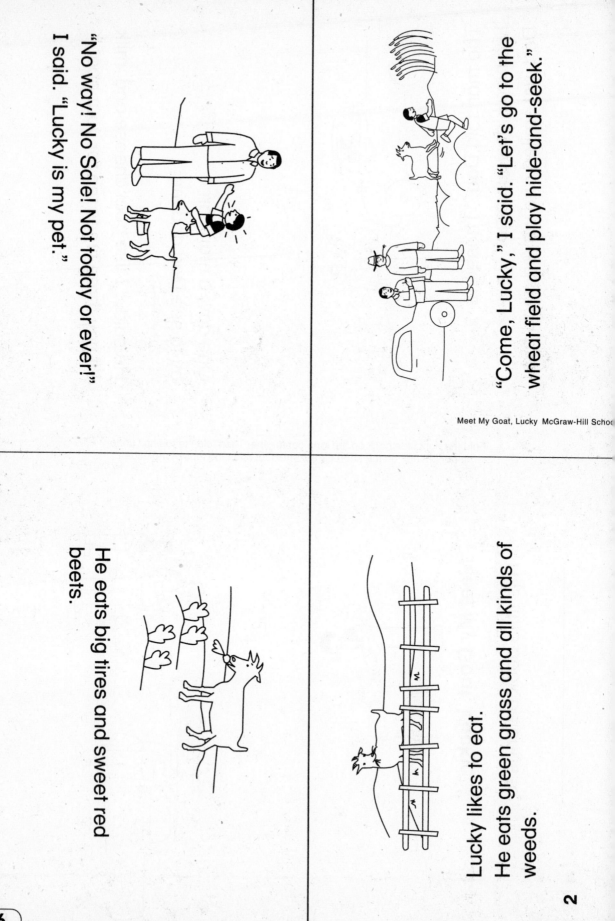

"Come, Lucky," I said. "Let's go to the
wheat field and play hide-and-seek."

Meet My Goat, Lucky McGraw-Hill School

He eats big tires and sweet red
beets.

Lucky likes to eat.
He eats green grass and all kinds of
weeds.

Name _____ Date _____

Listen for /ü/

Draw a circle around the pictures whose names have the same vowel sound as in spoon.

/ü/oo, ue, ew

Find the word in the box that will finish each sentence. Write it on the
line.

blue	broom	chew	threw	goose
Moo	mood	moose	room	true

1. Mom gave me a _____ and said, "Sweep up!"

2. But first, I had to pick up my red and _____ coat.

3. Then I _____ out some trash.

4. What Mom said was _____.

5. My _____ was messy.

6. One day a honking _____ sat next to a fence.

7. Then a cow came by and said, "_____."

8. Next came a _____ with its big horns.

9. It began to _____ on some grass.

10. All of them were happy and in a good _____.

Name_____ Date_____

/ü/ oo, ue, ew

Draw a circle around the word to finish each sentence. Then write the word on the line.

1. Mom asks, "Are you wearing —————— shoes?"

                                    nine   new   noon

2. I —————— one inch since last fall.

groom   gave   grew

3. My library books are —————— today.

                      day   doe   due

4. My girl scout —————— is going on a field trip.

           true   troop   tooth

5. We will go to the ——————.

                 zoo   zoom   zip

6. In school, I —————— a picture of a funny clown.

           drop   drew   dew

7. I don't have a —————— where my cat is.

           chew   clue   cool

8. Sometimes the —————— is full.

           make   mile   moon

9. Mom bought me a —————— jacket.

           blue   back   block

10. "We are having —————— tonight."

stew   shoe   spoon

/ü/ *oo, ue, ew*

Draw a line to the word that answers each riddle. Then draw a circle around the letters in the word that stand for the vowel sound.

1. You wear these in the snow.   pool

2. You see this at night.   true

3. When you eat, you do this.   new

4. This word also means real.   loose

5. You can swim in this.   chew

6. This is the opposite of old.   tool

7. This is the opposite of tight.   boots

8. This is used in doing work.   spoon

9. You use this to eat ice cream.   noon

10. This is another way of saying 12 o'clock.   moon

Listen for /ou/ and /oi/

Draw a circle around the picture whose name has the same vowel sound as the first picture in each row.

Name _____ Date _____

/ou/ou, ow and /oi/oi, oy

Find the word in the box that will finish each sentence. Write it on the line.

how	sound	flowers	down	soil
toy	around	enjoy	join	found

1. I love to plant _____ .

2. I feel good when my hands are in the _____ .

3. My friends often _____ me in my garden.

4. I show them _____ to weed and plant.

5. We _____ working together.

6. One night, I heard a _____ and woke up.

7. I looked _____ my room.

8. Then I _____ out what happened.

9. Something had fallen _____ .

10. It was my _____ clown.

/ou/ *ou, ow* and /oi/ *oi, oy*

Draw a line to the word that answers each riddle. Then draw a circle around the letters in the word that stand for the vowel sound.

1. This means "a bit wet."   gown

2. This is another word for lad.   trout

3. The letters *a, e, i ,o* and *u* are
   called this.   coins

4. This is where people live and
   work.   oil

5. This is a kind of fish.   boy

6. This is something a car
   needs.   moist

7. Dimes and nickels are called
   this.   join

8. You play with these.   vowels

9. This is a woman's dress.   town

10. This means to put two things
    together.   toys

Name _____ Date _____

ou/*ou, ow* and /oi/*oi, oy*

Read each sentence. Add the missing letters to the word. Then write the word on the line.

ou	ow	oi	oy

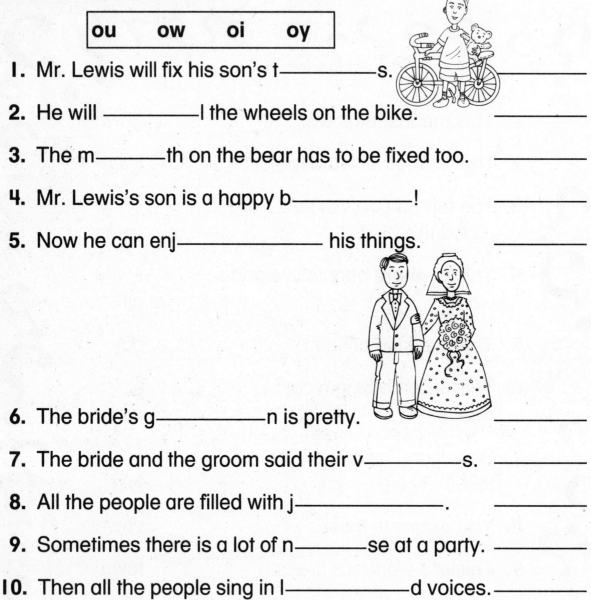

1. Mr. Lewis will fix his son's t————s. _____

2. He will ————l the wheels on the bike. _____

3. The m————th on the bear has to be fixed too. _____

4. Mr. Lewis's son is a happy b————! _____

5. Now he can enj———— his things. _____

6. The bride's g————n is pretty. _____

7. The bride and the groom said their v————s. _____

8. All the people are filled with j————. _____

9. Sometimes there is a lot of n————se at a party. _____

10. Then all the people sing in l————d voices. _____

Name_____ Date_____

Listen for /ôr/ and /îr/

Draw a circle around each picture whose name has the same vowel sound as in *hear*. Draw a line under each picture whose name has the same vowel sound as in *horn*.

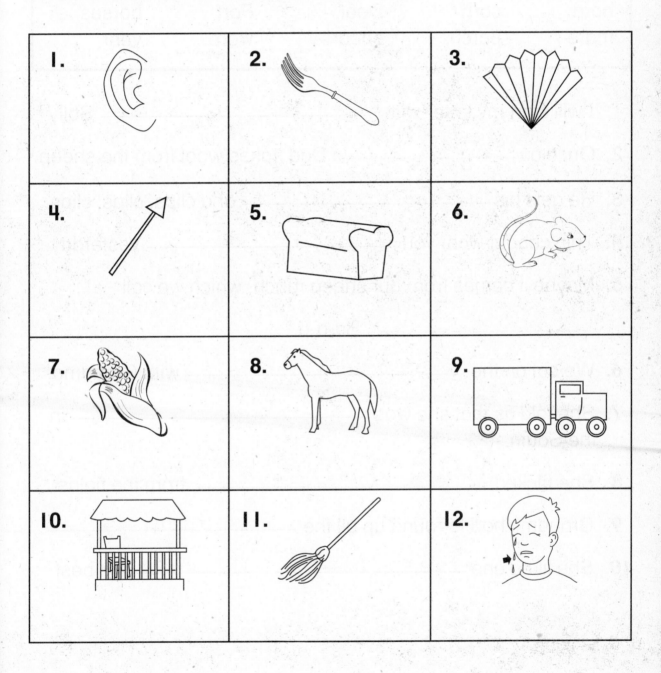

/âr/ are, /ôr/ or, ore and /îr/ ear

Find the word in the box that will finish each sentence. Write it on the line.

born	corn	Dear	Fort	horses
mare	porch	shears	wore	year

1. I will start my letter with "_____ Sally."

2. Once a _____ Dad takes wool from the sheep.

3. He gets his _____ and clips, clips, clips.

4. Think about what you _____ yesterday.

5. Maybe it comes from our sheep ranch, which we call

   "_____ Ba-a-a."

6. We sat on the _____ with Grandma.

7. She told us that she was _____ in the South.

8. She picked _____ from the fields.

9. Grandma had to round up all the _____.

10. She liked one _____ the best.

/âr/ are, /ôr/ or, ore and /îr/ ear

Draw a line to the word that answers each riddle. Then draw a circle around the letters in the word that stand for the vowel sound.

1. This is what you pay to get on the bus.   store

2. You use your ears to do this.   spear

3. You can shop at this place.   fork

4. Some people make this noise when they sleep.   fare

5. This is the opposite of far.   snore

6. This is a long pole with a point at the end.   hear

7. This is the opposite of front.   short

8. You eat with this.   more

9. This is not long or tall.   near

10. This is greater in number.   rear

Name _____ Date _____

/âr/ *are*, /ôr/ *or, ore* and /îr/ *ear*

Read each sentence. Add the missing letters to the word. Then write the word on the line.

are	or	ore	ear

1. When you talk, try to speak cl———ly. _____

2. Then your friends will be able to h———. _____

3. Tell them about the day you got lost at

   the sh———. _____

4. Try to keep your talk sh———t. _____

5. You don't want people to get b———d. _____

6. It is rainy this m———ning. _____

7. Mom asked me to s———t the clothes. _____

8. Oops, I t——— a sheet. _____

9. I hope Mom doesn't c———. _____

10. "That sheet was old and w———n
    anyway," she said.

Listen for /är/ and /ûr/

Draw a circle around the picture whose name has the same vowel sound as the first picture in each row.

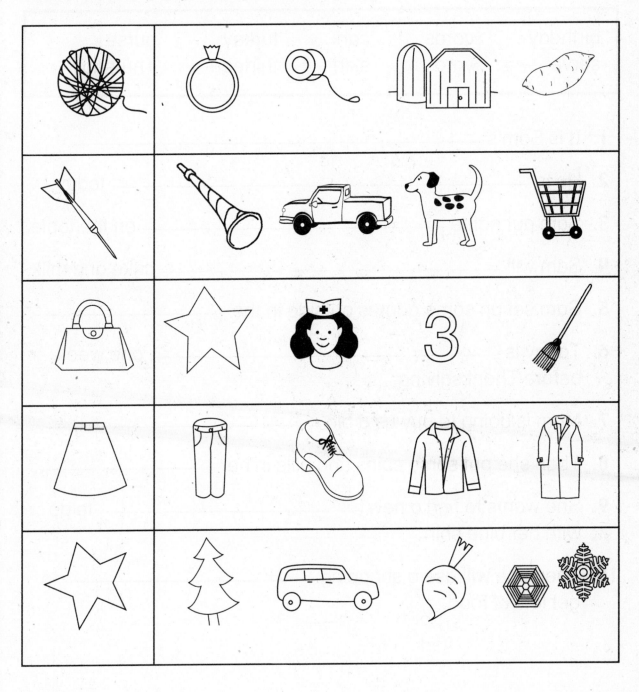

Name _____ Date _____

/är/ *ar* and /ûr/ *ir, ur, er*

Find the word in the box that will finish each sentence. Write it on the line.

birthday	cards	cart	turkey	purse
serve	yard	skirt	thirteen	Thursday

1. It is Sam's _____ .

2. He is _____ today.

3. Sam put name _____ on the table.

4. Sam will _____ cake and milk.

5. Sam set up some games outside in the _____ .

6. Today is _____ , one week before Thanksgiving.

7. Mom is going to buy us a big _____ .

8. Then she put some coins and bills in her _____ .

9. She wants to find a new _____ to go with her blue shirt.

10. Then she will use a shopping _____ to get lots of food.

/är/ ar and /ûr/ir, ur, er

Draw a line to the word that answers each riddle. Then draw a circle around the letters in the word that stand for the vowel sound.

1. This has strings to pluck.   bark

2. It has a sharp point.   fern

3. Flowers grow here.   skirt

4. This is part of a tree.   dart

5. This is to cause pain.   carpet

6. This is what a girl would wear.   bird

7. This is a kind of plant.   hurt

8. It covers a floor.   harp

9. It may nest in a tree.   garden

/är/ *ar* and /ûr/ *ir, ur, er*

Draw a circle around the word that will finish each sentence.
Write the word on the line.

1. I saw a ————————————— of wild horses.

   herd   smoke   horn

2. They ran so fast, they kicked up the ———————————.

   dog   dirt   dorm

3. Then they ran behind a bunch of ——————— trees.

   first   flag   fir

4. We came to a ————————————— in the road
   and couldn't see them.

   curve   cart   case

5. Ari won ————————————— place in spelling.

   third   train   tried

6. We have a ————————————— in a cage.

   bird   burn   best

7. It ————————————————— a lot.

   cooks   churches   chirps

8. Do you know that *jump* is a —————————?

   vase   cook   verb

9. Now I have to ————————————— the paints.

   stir   start   stem

Review /ü/; /oi/; /âr/; /ôr/; /îr/; /ûr/

Draw a circle around the word that answers each riddle.

1. You do this when you eat.
sleep   chew   chase

2. Use this on a creaky gate.
oil   boil   toil

3. It helps light the way.
horse   mare   torch

4. This is a pair of pants and a jacket.
suit   sit   soup

5. This is a kind of look.
fear   cry   stare

6. This is a sound from a bird.
chirp   chop   churn

7. This is what you can do to water.
soil   boil   foil

8. A car needs this to run.
fuel   food   first

9. This lives in a shell.
turtle   hare   bird

10. This brings a lot of wind and rain.
steam   stem   storm

Name ______________________ Date ____________

Review /ü/; /ou/; /oi/; /ôr/; /îr/; /ûr/

Name each picture. Find its name in the word box.
Then write the word in the puzzle.

house	crown	turnips	spool	horn
spoon	corn	pouch	thirteen	curls

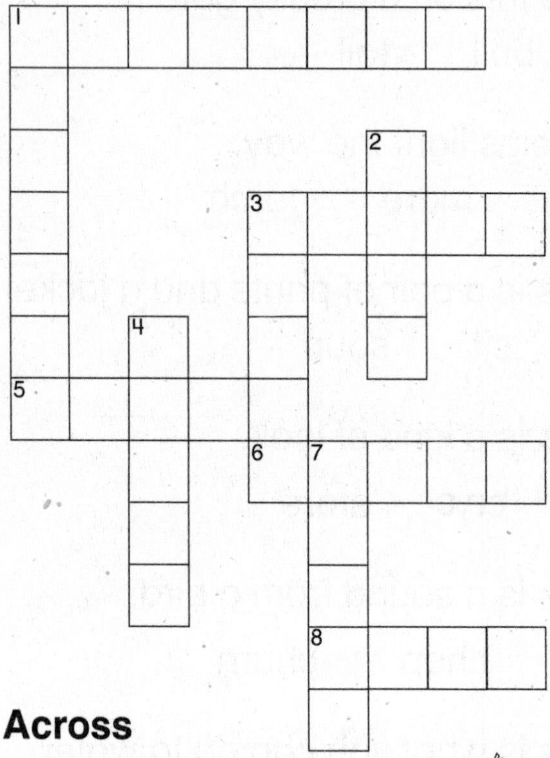

Across

1. 

3. 

5. 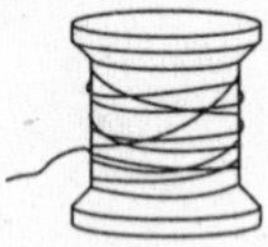

6. 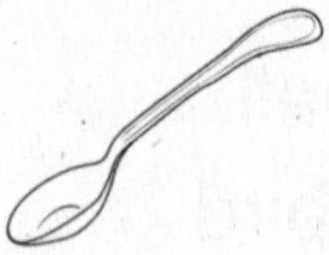

8. 

Down

1. 

2. 

3. 

4. 

7. 

/10

Name _____ Date _____

Review /ü/; /ou/; /oi/; /âr/; /är/; /ûr/

Draw a circle around the missing letters in each word. Write the letters on the lines.

1. A n————n is a person, place or thing.   ur   ou   oi

2. The letters *a, e, i, o,* and *u* are v————els.   ow   ar   oi

3. Miss Green said the class was too
   l————d.   ur   ou   oi

4. We have to keep our v————ces low.   ow   ou   oi

5. Miss Green c————s a lot about us.   ur   are   ir

6. We can c————nt by tens.   ue   oi   ou

7. We f————nd out about fish.   ue   ur   ou

8. One kind of fish is called a c————p.   ar   ir   ur

9. One kind of fish is a tr————t.   ue   oo   ou

10. S————n it will be three o'clock.   oo   ou   ur

Review /ü/; /ou/; /oi/; /âr/; /ôr/; /îr/; /ûr/; /är/

Draw a circle around the word that names or tells about
each picture.

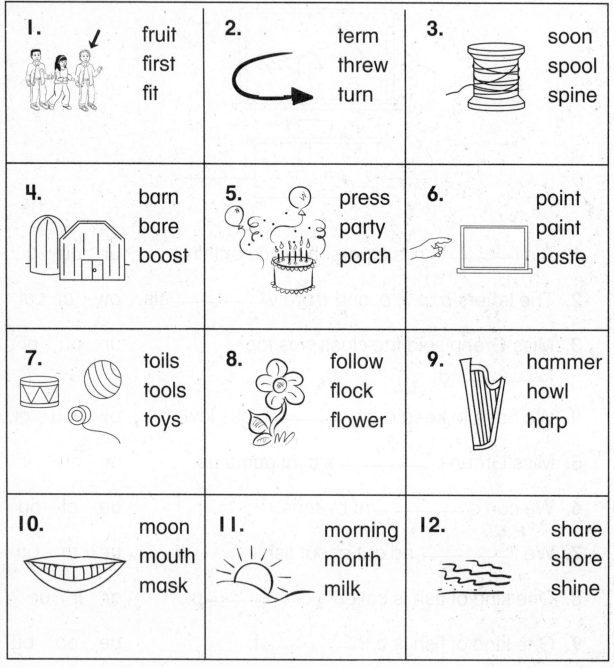

1. fruit / first / fit	**2.** term / threw / turn	**3.** soon / spool / spine
4. barn / bare / boost	**5.** press / party / porch	**6.** point / paint / paste
7. toils / tools / toys	**8.** follow / flock / flower	**9.** hammer / howl / harp
10. moon / mouth / mask	**11.** morning / month / milk	**12.** share / shore / shine

66 Review Variant Vowels /ü/ *oo*; /ou/ *ou, ow*;
/oi/ *oi, oy*; /âr/ *are*; /ôr/ *or*; /îr/ *ear*; /ûr/ *ir, er, ur*; /är/ *ar*

Grade 2   12

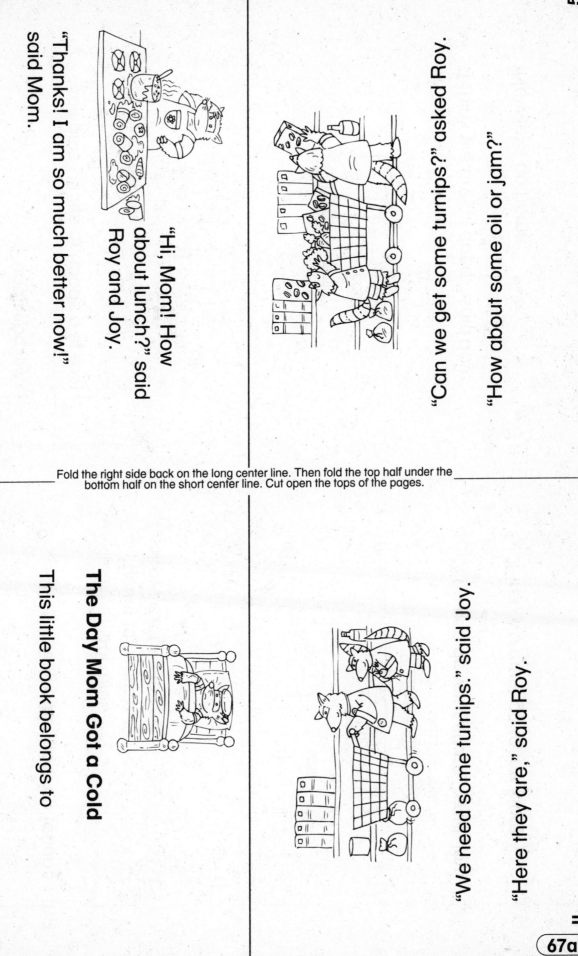

"Hi, Mom! How about lunch?" said Roy and Joy.

"Thanks! I am so much better now!" said Mom.

"Can we get some turnips?" asked Roy.

"How about some oil or jam?"

Fold the right side back on the long center line. Then fold the top half under the bottom half on the short center line. Cut open the tops of the pages.

The Day Mom Got a Cold

This little book belongs to

_____

"We need some turnips." said Joy.

"Here they are," said Roy.

"I think we are all done," said Joy.

"Now let's go home."

"Here is a spoon to stir it," said Joy.

"It will boil soon."

The Day Mom Got a Cold McGraw-Hill Schoo

"You can do your share," said Joy.

"First, we must go to the store."

"Let's make Mom a stew for lunch," said Joy.

"But I cannot do that!" said Roy.

Silent Letters

Say the name of each picture. Then draw a circle around the silent letter or letters.

1. lamb	**2.** knight	**3.** knit
4. half	**5.** write	**6.** limb
7. comb	**8.** school	**9.** knife

Name _____ Date _____

Silent Letters

Find the word in the box that will finish each sentence. Write it on the line. Then draw a circle around the silent letter or letters.

climbing	gnat	high	knights	know
light	limbs	night	lamb	wrote

1. The moon comes out at _____.

2. Most _____ rode horses.

3. Long ago, people _____ with quills.

4. A _____ is a tiny insect.

5. Who is _____ up the ladder?

6. If you can lift the bar, then it must be _____.

7. A _____ is a young sheep.

8. I am almost five feet _____.

9. Your legs and arms are _____. Move them!

10. Do you _____ how to count by 3's?

Silent Letters

Draw a circle around the word that will finish each sentence. Then write it in the line.

1. I am _____ a story.
   wrote   writing   wrapping

2. It is about a boat _____.
   wrist   waiter   wreck

3. It takes place at _____.
   night   sight   tight

4. A man on the boat sees something _____.
   fight   night   light

5. But it is a little _____ flying under a pillow case.
   wrist   wren   write

6. I _____ it is a silly story, but it is fun.
   note   night   know

7. I fell and hurt my _____.
   wrap   write   wrist

8. The doctor will _____ it up.
   wore   wrote   wrap

9. I still can't turn a _____.
   knob   kind   knight

10. I also can't _____ my hair well.
    lamb   comb   crash

Silent Letters

Draw a line to the word that answers each riddle. Then draw a circle around the silent letter or letters.

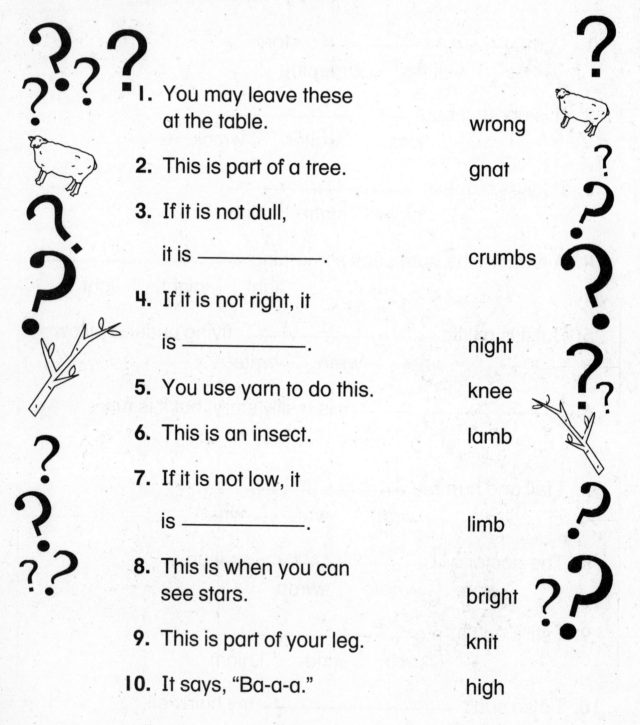

1. You may leave these at the table.

   wrong

2. This is part of a tree.

   gnat

3. If it is not dull, it is _____.

   crumbs

4. If it is not right, it is _____.

   night

5. You use yarn to do this.

   knee

6. This is an insect.

   lamb

7. If it is not low, it is _____.

   limb

8. This is when you can see stars.

   bright

9. This is part of your leg.

   knit

10. It says, "Ba-a-a."

Listen for /ər/

Name each picture. Draw a circle around each picture whose name has the vowel sound you hear at the end of *dollar*.

Identify /ər/er, or, ar

Draw lines to connect each picture to a word. Then draw a circle around the letters that stand for the same vowel sound you hear at the end of *dollar*.

1.   glider

2.   leopard

3.   helicopter

4.   collar

5.   beekeeper

6.   markers

7.   sailor

8.   hammer

9.   diver

10.   hanger

Identify /ər/er, or, ar

Draw a circle around the word that will finish each sentence. Then draw a line under the letters that stand for the sound you hear at the end of *dollar*.

1. Our _____, Miss Knapp, helps us do a lot of things.

   teacher   twenty   tablet

2. She gave me a set of _____.

   marks   markers   markets

3. It had all kinds of _____.

   colors   powder   crates

4. Miss Knapp teaches us good _____.

   hangers   hammers   manners

5. We thanked the _____ for visiting our class.

   marker   mayor   motor

6. We are finding out about life in a _____.

   dream   desert   drain

7. We made _____ hats yesterday.

   pasted   power   paper

8. My _____ liked my hat.

   hanger   major   mother

9. My _____ likes to hear about my day at school.

   father   collar   younger

Identify /ər/er, or, ar

Draw a circle around the letters that will finish the word in each
sentence. Then write the word on the line.

1. I have five one doll———— bills.

   _____   ar   or   er

2. My sist———— said I should save them.

   _____   ar   or   er

3. My broth———— said I should spend them.

   _____   ar   or   er

4. My moth———— said I should do what I want.

   _____   ar   or   er

5. I think I will buy a rubb———— raft.

   _____   ar   or   er

6. Did you know that airplanes are kept in
   hang———— s?

   _____   ar   or   er

7. Do you hang your clothes on hang———— s ?

   _____   ar   or   er

8. Try not to eat too much sug———— .

   _____   ar   or   er

9. What flav———— yogurt do you like best?

   _____   ar   or   er

Listen for Short *e: ea*

Draw a circle around each picture whose name has the short *e* sound as in *head*.

1.	2.	3.
4.	5.	6.
7.	8.	9.
10.	11.	12.

Name _____ Date _____

Identify Short *e: ea*

Find the word in the box that will finish each sentence. Write it on the line.

bread	breakfast	breath	ready	head
healthy	read	spread	heavy	weather

1. This morning, I had two slices of ————————————.

2. I ———————————— jam on each one.

3. Mom always says I should eat a good ——————————.

4. Last week, she ———————————— a book about eating well.

5. She wants me to be ————————————.

6. My Dad is a little too ————————————.

7. Some days he wears a hat on his ————————————.

8. Then he jogs in the park, but only in good ——————————.

9. Sometimes he gets out of ————————————.

10. That's when he says, "I am ———————————— to stop."

Identify Short *e: ea*

Draw a line to the word that answers each riddle. Then draw a circle around the letters that stand for the short *e* sound.

1. This is the opposite of *alive*.

2. Some pipes are made of this.

3. You use this to hem pants.

4. This keeps you warm.

5. A doctor's job is to keep you in good ____.

6. To know what to wear, you need this kind of report.

7. Many belts are made of this.

8. This is a field of grassy land.

• lead

• leather

• health

• weather

• dead

• thread

• sweater

• meadow

Name_____ Date_____

Short *e: ea*

Draw a line under the word that will finish each sentence.

1. Two —————— are better than one.

   heeds   heads   hoes

2. Birds of a —————— flock together.

   feather   feeder   feat

3. Half a loaf is better than no ——————.

   bed   bead   bread

4. The rock was too —————— to lift.

   head   heavy   heat

5. When I stretch, I —————— my arms out wide.

   speed   spread   read

6. I —————— a book about how to draw.

   ride   read   reason

7. I never get out of —————— when I jump rope.

   bean   bread   breath

8. The —————— was filled with flowers.

   meat   matter   meadow

9. I wear my boots in cold ——————.

   weather   feather   leather

10. I will use —————— to stitch a button on my coat.

   bread   read   thread

Listen for Long *e: y, ey*

Draw a circle around the pictures whose names have the same long *e* sound as in key.

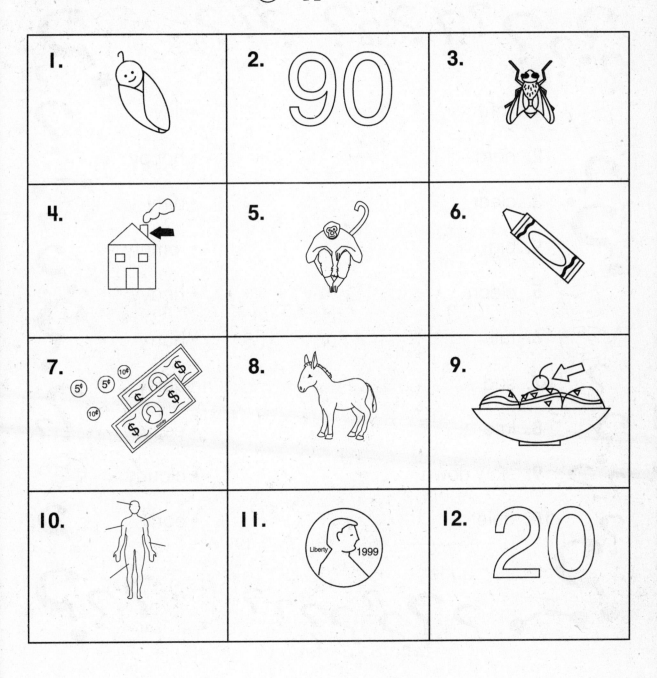

Long *e: y, ey*

Draw lines to connect the opposites.

1. light   • tiny

2. hard   • happy

3. clear   • dirty

4. big   • empty

5. clean   • heavy

6. full   • hurry

7. sad   • noisy

8. late   • easy

9. slow down   • cloudy

10. quiet   • early

Long *e: y, ey*

Write the word that will finish each sentence. Then draw a circle around the letters that stand for the long e sound.

cloudy	donkey	funny	key	library
lucky	monkey	study	windy	worry

1. One _____ day, I went to the park to fly my kite.

2. That's when I saw a boy riding on a _____.

3. Then a man came by with a chattering _____.

4. It had a _____ hat on its head.

5. The monkey stole the _____ to my house!

6. But I was very _____. The man got it back for me.

7. Then the sky turned _____.

8. Mom would _____ if I didn't get home soon.

9. Dad is going to take me to the _____ to get some books.

10. Then I have to sit at my desk and _____.

Name_____ Date_____

Long e: y, ey

Draw a circle around the word that will finish each sentence.

1. Mom gets up _____ to start cooking.

   hurry   early   hearing

2. Mom wants everything to taste good. Dad says

   she is too _____.

   lonely   frankly   fussy

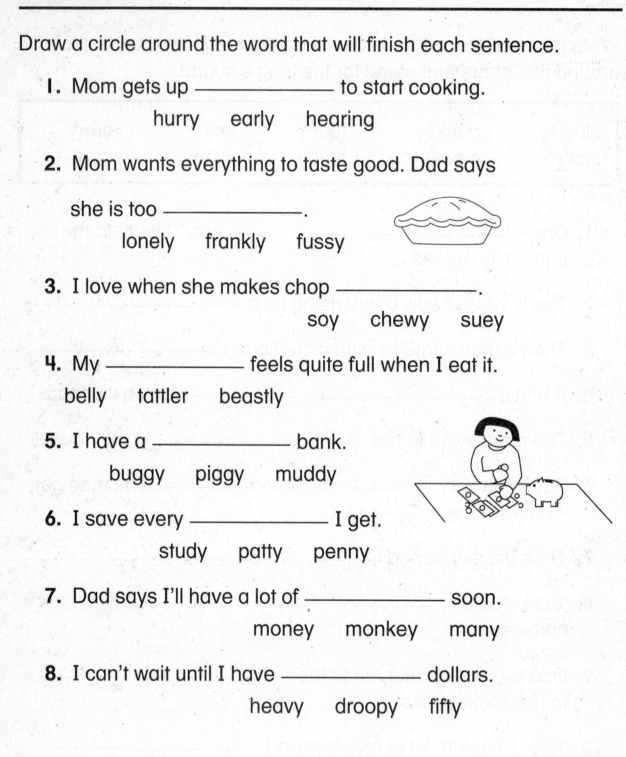

3. I love when she makes chop _____.

   soy   chewy   suey

4. My _____ feels quite full when I eat it.

   belly   tattler   beastly

5. I have a _____ bank.

   buggy   piggy   muddy

6. I save every _____ I get.

   study   patty   penny

7. Dad says I'll have a lot of _____ soon.

   money   monkey   many

8. I can't wait until I have _____ dollars.

   heavy   droopy   fifty

Name _____ Date _____

Review /ər/; Long *e*; Short *e*; Silent Letters

Find the name of each picture in the box. Write it on the line.

bread	comb	dollar	feather	thread
half	knife	markers	sixty	

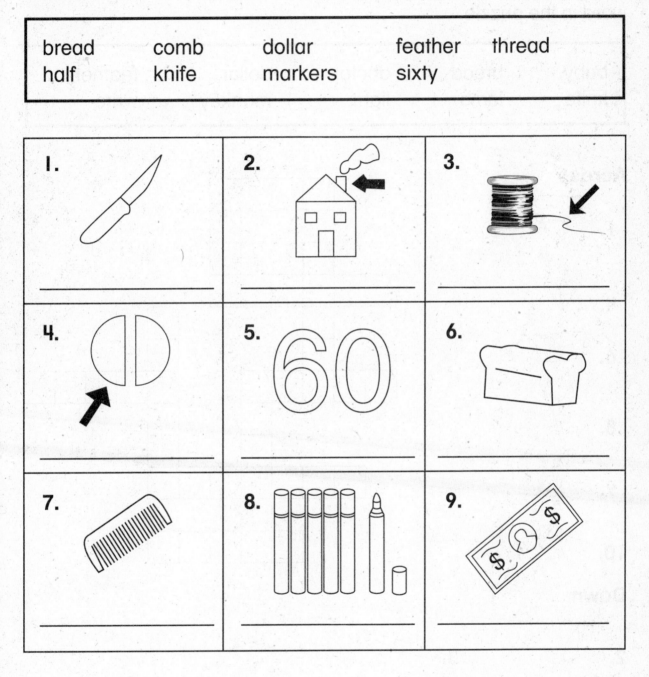

1. _____

2. _____

3. _____

4. _____

5. _____

6. _____

7. _____

8. _____

9. _____

Review / ər/; Long *e*; Short *e*; Silent Letters

Name each picture. Find its name in the word box. Then write the word in the puzzle.

baby	bread	doctor	dollar	feather
knife	lamb	light	monkey	write

Across

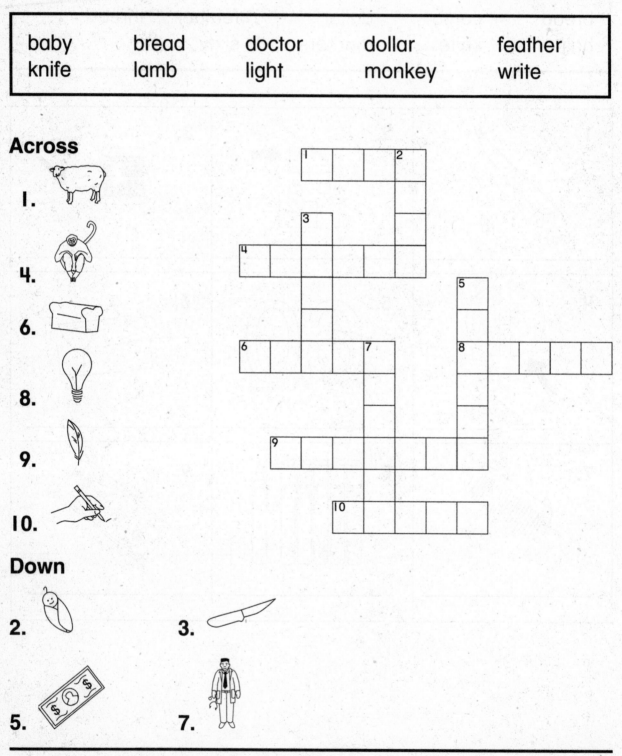

1.

4.

6.

8.

9.

10.

Down

2.

3.

5.

7.

Grade 2

Name _____ Date _____

Review /ər/; Long *e*; Short *e*; Silent Letters

Read each sentence. Add the missing letter or letters to complete the word. Then write the word on the line.

1. My sister said she will ——nit me some socks.—————————

2. I will ——rite her a thank you note. ——————————

3. Maybe I can make her a new h——dband. ——————————

4. I can make one with a l——ther strap. ——————————

5. I think I will ask the tail—— how to stitch it. ——————————

6. Mom asked me to take care of the bab——. ——————————

7. She likes to clim—— the stairs. ——————————

8. She ——nows I will not let her fall. ——————————

9. She loves her little monk——. ——————————

10. I love my baby sist——. ——————————

Name _____ Date _____

Review / ər/; Long *e*; Short *e*; Silent Letters

Draw a circle around the word that names or tells about
the picture.

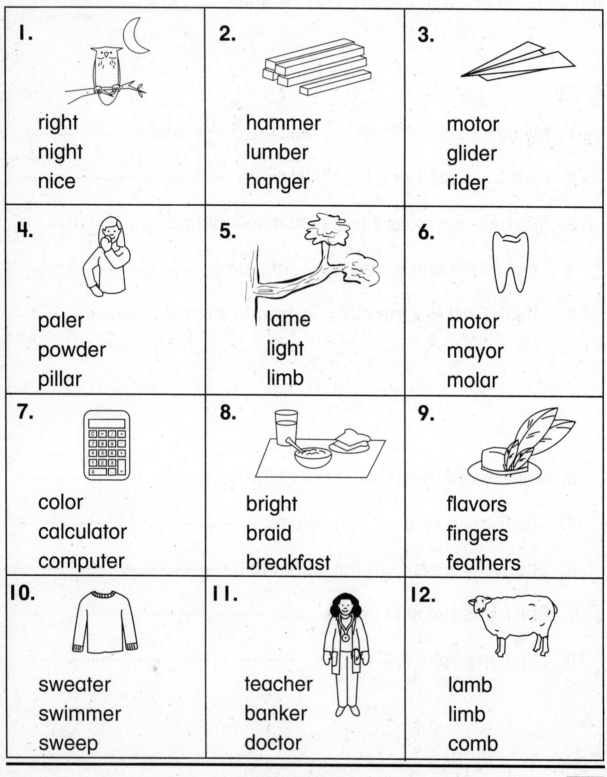

1.
right
night
nice

2.
hammer
lumber
hanger

3.
motor
glider
rider

4.
paler
powder
pillar

5.
lame
light
limb

6.
motor
mayor
molar

7.
color
calculator
computer

8.
bright
braid
breakfast

9.
flavors
fingers
feathers

10.
sweater
swimmer
sweep

11.
teacher
banker
doctor

12.
lamb
limb
comb

"Look! I see a bluebird's feather," said Robert. "You win!"

"You win!" said Peter.

"Why don't you put your heads together?" said Father. "Come up with a bright idea."

Fold the right side back on the long center line. Then fold the top half under the bottom half on the short center line. Cut open the tops of the pages.

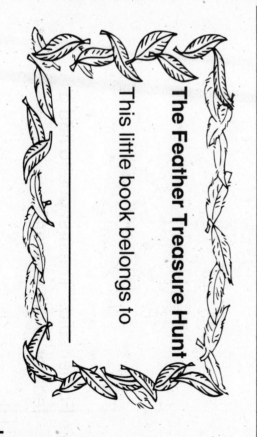

The Feather Treasure Hunt

This little book belongs to

_____

Robert saw a wren fly by. But he did not see a feather.

Peter said, "My brain is asleep."
"I have an idea," said Robert.

Robert went to his backpack and took out some bread. He spread crumbs on the ground.

The Feather Treasure Hunt McGraw-Hill Scho

Peter climbed the limb of a tree.
He looked high and low.

Father said, "The first one to find a feather is the winner."

Listen for /u̇/oo

Mark an **X** on the pictures whose names have the sound for *oo* as in took.

Introduce /ù/oo

Draw a circle around the word that will finish each sentence.
Write it on the line.

1. We _____ Grandma to the play.

   too   took   tone

2. We had a _____ time.

   good   goal   give

3. It was so funny, we _____ with laughter.

   soon   shook   send

4. It was about a girl who wrote a _____.

   bad   book   best

5. At the end of the play, we _____
   and clapped.   store   stop   stood

6. Tad lives in a nice _____.

   neighborhood   newspaper   note

7. The _____ are behind his house.

   wool   woods   with

8. There is a little _____ there.

   book   brook   brake

9. He sits and reads in the quiet _____.

   cook   nook   nice

10. He _____ around and smiles.

   cooks   hooks   looks

Introduce /ŭ/oo

Draw a circle around the word that answers each riddle. Then write it on the line.

1. This word means the opposite of bad. _____

   gone   good   gold

2. You hang your coat on this. _____

   hoof   hoop   hook

3. If you didn't sit, maybe you did this. _____

   shook   stood   good

4. Oak and pine are two different kinds of this. _____

   boots   wood   could

5. This is another name for a cow's foot. _____

   hoof   hoot   roof

6. It is something you can read. _____

   boat   book   brook

7. You use your eyes to do this. _____

   look   lake   lock

8. This is a cozy place. _____

   look   nook   nice

9. This can cover your head. _____

   hoop   food   hood

10. You do this to food. _____

   cry   coop   cook

Introduce /ǔ/oo

Draw a circle around the word in each sentence that has the same vowel sound as in *foot*. Then write the word on the line.

1. The new space movie was showing in my neighborhood.

   _____

2. My uncle took us to see it.

   _____

3. We stood in line for an hour to get in. _____

4. We all thought it was really good. _____

5. Next week we will go to a football game. _____

6. I went camping with Grandpa in

   the woods. _____

7. Grandpa says I grew a foot since

   last year. _____

8. We found a quiet nook to set up

   our tent. _____

9. We fished in the little brook nearby. _____

10. We cooked our supper over a campfire.

    _____

Name_____ Date_____

Listen for Soft *c* and Soft *g*

Draw a circle around the pictures whose names have the soft *g* sound as in *age*. Draw a line under the pictures whose names have the soft *c* sound as in *ice*.

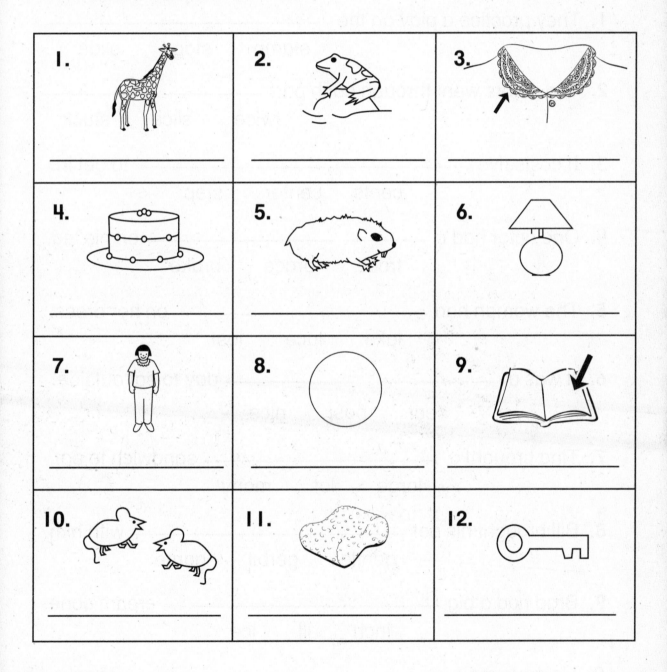

1.	2.	3.
_____	_____	_____
4.	5.	6.
_____	_____	_____
7.	8.	9.
_____	_____	_____
10.	11.	12.
_____	_____	_____

Name _____ Date _____

Soft *c* and Soft *g*

Draw a circle around the word that will finish each sentence.
Write it on the line.

1. They practice a play on the _____.

   stamp   stage   slide

2. The actors went through each part _____.

   twice   slice   stuck

3. It costs five _____ to get in.

   cents   center   step

4. One actor had a _____ on his leg.

   trace   brace   brake

5. The woman had _____ on her dress.

   lake   lace   lost

6. It was a _____ day to eat outside.

   neat   post   nice

7. Tina brought a _____ sandwich to eat.

   large   lot   many

8. Bill brought his pet _____ with him.

   gentle   gerbil   game

9. Brad had a big _____ cream cone.

   inch   ill   ice

10. He gave me a _____ of cake.

    slide   slice   slip

Soft *c* and Soft *g*

Name each picture. Write **ce** if you hear the soft *c* sound as in *ice*.
Write **ge** if you hear the soft *g* sound as in *page*.

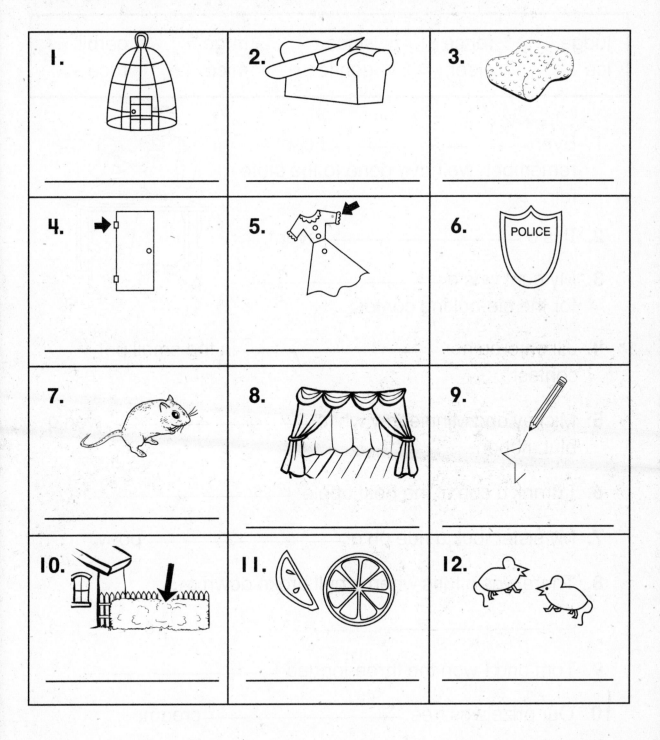

1.	2.	3.
_____	_____	_____
4.	5.	6. POLICE
_____	_____	_____
7.	8.	9.
_____	_____	_____
10.	11.	12.
_____	_____	_____

Soft c and Soft g

Find the word in the box that will finish each sentence. Write it on the line.

judge	fence	since	huge	gerbil
ice	cider	gentle	mice	race

1. Ever _____ I can remember, we have gone to the state fair.

2. It is a _____ event.

3. My aunt was a _____ for the pie-baking contest.

4. Jill entered her _____ in the small pet contest.

5. Mickey and Minnie, my white _____, won a blue ribbon.

6. I drank a cup of the best apple _____.

7. My sister took a ride on a _____ pony.

8. There was a fuss when a bull broke down a

   _____.

9. Tom and I won the three-legged _____.

10. Our prize was free _____ cream.

Listen for /ô/

In each row, draw a circle around the pictures whose names have the same vowel sound as in *claw*.

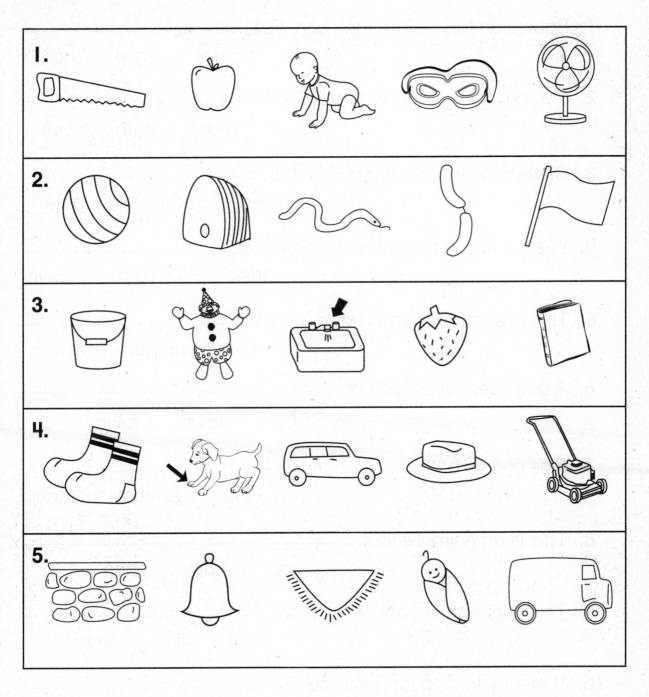

1.

2.

3.

4.

5.

Name _____ Date _____

/ô/a, au, aw

Draw a circle around the word that answers each riddle. Then
write it on the line.

1. Babies do this before they can walk. _____

                                         carry   crawl   comb

2. You need this in order to play catch. _____

                                         back   bath   ball

3. Something that is very bad is this. _____

                                  sawed   awful   daughter

4. It is the time when the sun comes up. _____

                                  dusk   daylight   dawn

5. This is someone who writes a book. _____

                                    fall   author   crawl

6. A baby deer is called this. _____

                            fall   dawn   fawn

7. This comes between July and September. _____

                              June   August   March

8. This is an animal's foot. _____

                          pat   paw   pace

9. This might be in front of a house. _____

                              lace   like   lawn

10. It means to stop for a minute. _____

                          pork   pause   hawk

/ô/a, au, aw

Draw a circle around the word to finish the sentence. Then write it on the line.

1. Sue stayed home _____ she was sick.

           blast   because   believe

2. She said, "It is not my _____!"

              flake   halt   fault

3. She watched her baby sister _____.

              can   cause   crawl

4. Sue heard a noise from the _____.

              hunt   hop   hall

5. Her cat was licking its _____.

    paws   packs   pans

6. Ned is very _____.

       tell   till   tall

7. He drinks his milk with a _____.

          straw   saw   spot

8. He plays _____ with his friends.

       bill   ball   bell

9. He sits on the _____ and reads a book.

     line   lane   lawn

10. He has two favorite _____.

      after   antlers   authors

/ô/a, au, aw

Find the word in the box that goes with each picture. Write it on the line.

crawl	claw	fawn	straw	wall	yawn
sausage	fall	saucer	faucet	ball	shawl

1. _____

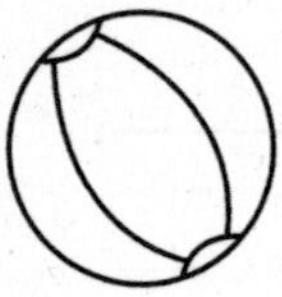

2. _____

3. _____

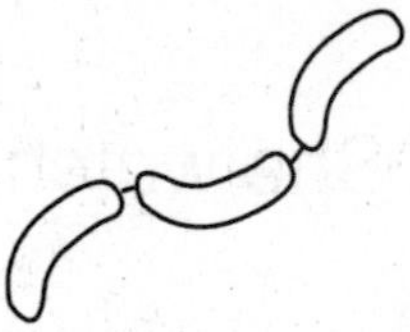

4. _____

5. _____

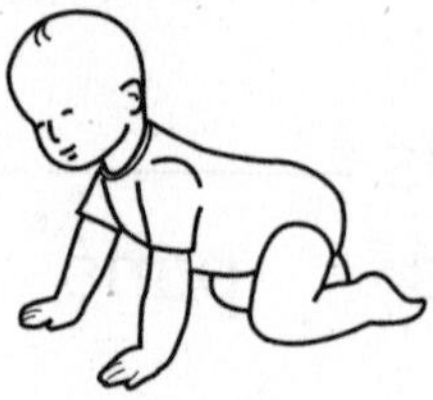

6. _____

7. _____

8. _____

9. _____

10. _____

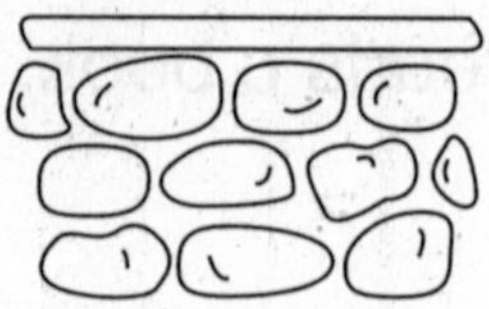

11. _____

12. _____

Listen for Digraphs

Mark an **X** on the pictures whose names have the sound of *ph* that you hear in *phone*. Draw a circle around the pictures whose names have the sound of *tch* that you hear in *watch*.

Digraphs *ph, tch*

Draw a circle around the word that will finish the sentence. Write it on the line.

1. Jill is serving a _____ of cookies.

   hatch   batch   home

2. Her socks don't _____ .

   match   make   hitch

3. There is a _____ of water on the table.

   peach   player   pitcher

4. What _____ is the moon in?

   photo   prize   phase

5. Will this _____ come out?

   phony   plate   photo

6. Phil _____ the boat to the jeep.

   hit   liked   hitched

7. Ann planted a vegetable _____ .

   pitch   patch   moat

8. She will _____ the plants carefully.

   watch   hike   wish

9. When did these baby chicks _____ ?

   catch   hatch   check

10. The chicks _____ in the dirt.

    scratch   catch   sport

Digraphs *ph, tch*

Draw a circle around the word that answers each riddle. Then write it on the line.

1. It means "go and get." _____

   fetch   pitch   feed

2. This can hold milk or water. _____

   patched   pitcher   paper

3. A place to cook _____

   pitcher   kitten   kitchen

4. A dancer must do this first. _____

   stitch   stretch   catch

5. Turn the light on with this. _____

   swap   snitch   switch

6. It means to grab. _____

   hitch   snatch   latch

7. A large animal _____

   elephant   photograph   telephone

8. It holds the door closed. _____

   fetch   match   latch

9. He throws the ball. _____

   stretcher   pitcher   checker

10. This is a kind of bird. _____

   photo   phony   pheasant

Digraphs *ph, tch*

Find the word in the box that goes with each picture. Write it on the line.

watch	scratch	catch	pitcher	switch
fetch	hatch	match	photo	

1. _____

2. _____

3. _____

4. _____

5. _____

6. _____

7. _____

8. _____

9. _____

Name_____ Date_____

Review /ù/oo and /ô/a, au, aw

Draw a circle around each word that has the same vowel sound as
the name of the picture.

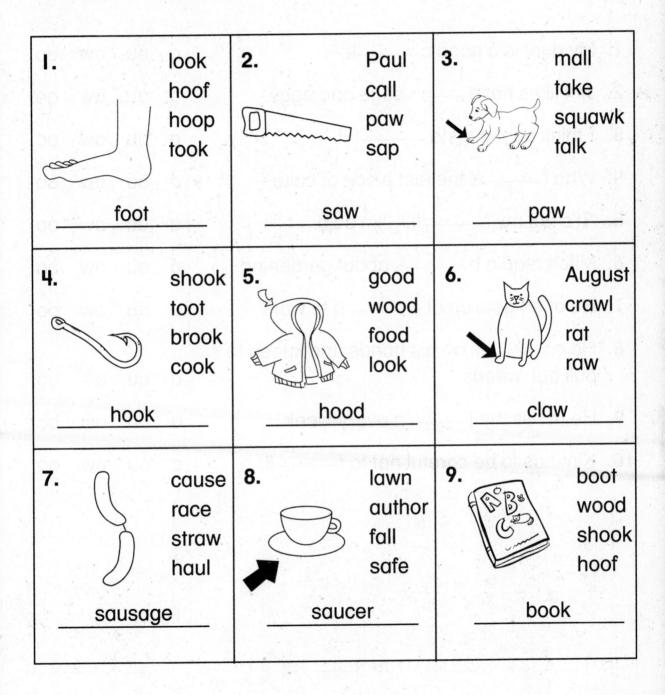

1. look
hoof
hoop
took

foot _____

2. Paul
call
paw
sap

saw _____

3. mall
take
squawk
talk

paw _____

4. shook
toot
brook
cook

hook _____

5. good
wood
food
look

hood _____

6. August
crawl
rat
raw

claw _____

7. cause
race
straw
haul

sausage _____

8. lawn
author
fall
safe

saucer _____

9. boot
wood
shook
hoof

book _____

Review /ů/oo and /ô/a, au, aw

Draw a circle around the letters that will finish the word in each
sentence. Write the letters on the line.

1. My aunt is a good c———k.   a   au   aw   oo

2. Jim likes her s———sage and eggs.   a   au   aw   oo

3. I think beans taste ———ful.   a   au   aw   oo

4. Who t———k the last piece of cake?   a   au   aw   oo

5. "It's not my f———lt," Jim said.   a   au   aw   oo

6. Mitch read a b———k about gardening.   a   au   aw   oo

7. He often gets up at d———n to work.   a   au   aw   oo

8. He cr———ls on his hands and knees to
   pull out weeds.   a   au   aw   oo

9. He mows the l———n every week.   a   au   aw   oo

10. Kim has to be careful not to f———ll.   a   au   aw   oo

Review Soft *c, g* and Digraphs *ph, tch*

Draw a circle around the name of each picture.

1.
photograph
elevator
elephant

2.
sponge
sprung
soap

3.
cake
coat
cage

4.
watch
catcher
scratch

5.
phony
photo
phone

6.
pitch
batch
patch

7.
switch
snatch
stitch

8.
jam
gems
games

9.
center
cell
cent

Name_____ Date_____

Review Soft *c, g* and Digraphs *ph, tch*

Draw a circle around the letters that will finish the word in each sentence. Write the letters on the line.

1. This is a ———oto of Mom and Dad.	ce ge ph tch
2. I taught my dog to fe———.	ce ge ph tch
3. Mom has a cell ———one in the van.	ce ge ph tch
4. My sister can ca——— better than anyone in our family.	ce ge ph tch
5. This horse is very ———ntle.	ce ge ph tch
6. Paul will hi——— the trailer to the car.	ce ge ph tch
7. Who will jud——— the contest?	ce ge ph tch
8. We ate lunch in the ki———en.	ce ge ph tch
9. Jo has seen the movie twi———.	ce ge ph tch
10. I love to eat chocolate fud———.	ce ge ph tch

Next we crossed a small brook. Then we trudged through a field. Suddenly a large brown bird flew up in front of us.

"Was that a hawk?" asked Madge. "It was large."

"No, look at the photo," said Paul. He pulled out the bird book. "It was a pheasant."

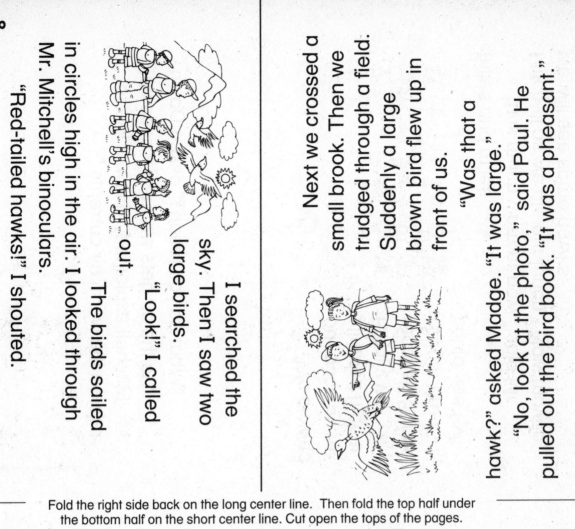

I searched the sky. Then I saw two large birds.

"Look!" I called out.

The birds sailed in circles high in the air. I looked through Mr. Mitchell's binoculars.

"Red-tailed hawks!" I shouted.

Fold the right side back on the long center line. Then fold the top half under the bottom half on the short center line. Cut open the tops of the pages.

It was cool in the woods. We passed under a huge crooked tree. Just then we saw a flash of red.

"Was that a hawk?" asked Dawn. "It had a red tail."

"No, that was a cardinal," said Paul. "A hawk is much larger," I said.

On Sunset Ridge

"Do you think we'll see any hawks?" I asked.

It was a nice fall day. We were hiking to Sunset Ridge.

Mr. Mitchell smiled. He is our scout leader. "I've seen them on Sunset Ridge once or twice," he said.

"What do you mean?" asked Dawn.

"As the air gets warmer, it rises up," Mr. Mitchell explained. "Hawks like to ride on the warm air currents."

On Sunset Ridge McGraw-Hill Schoo

Mr. Mitchell taught us a lot about hawks. My favorite is the red-tailed hawk.

Hawks like to perch in tall trees. They watch with their sharp eyes. All hawks

have sharp claws for catching mice.

for mice with their sharp claws for catching mice.

We slowed our pace as we climbed higher. Finally we reached Sunset Ridge. We could see for

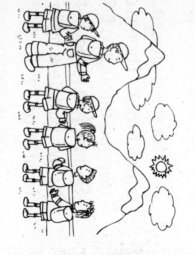

miles and miles.

"It is much warmer now," said Mr. Mitchell as we ate our lunch. "Now maybe we will see some hawks."

Hawks make their nests in tall trees, too. They lay two or three eggs. Soon the eggs hatch. Then the hawks catch more mice to feed their chicks.

Review r-controlled Variant Vowels /âr/are; /ôr/or, ore; /îr/ear

Find the word in the box that goes with each picture. Write it on the line.

tear	forehead	beard	fork	gear
square	organ	snore	ear	

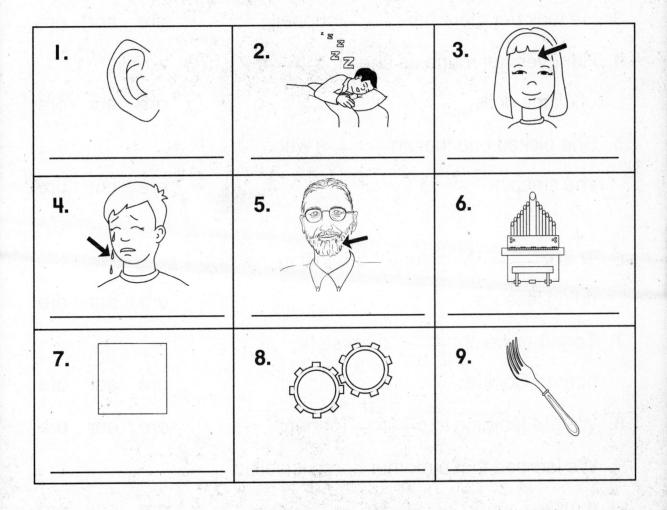

1. _____

2. _____

3. _____

4. _____

5. _____

6. _____

7. _____

8. _____

9. _____

Name _____ Date _____

Review r-controlled Variant Vowels /âr/*are*; /ôr/*or, ore*; /îr/*ear*

Draw a circle around the letters that will finish the word in each sentence. Write the letters on the line.

1. Ann was sad when her doll t_____.   are   ear   ore

2. Bart said he'd get her a new one

   at the toy st_____.   are   ear   ore

3. He took her there bef_____ supper.   are   ear   ore

4. Her eyes got round as she st _____d

   at all the dolls.   are   ear   ore

5. She picked one that sn_____s when

   she sleeps!   are   ear   ore

6. This y_____ Mitch and I are taking

   riding lessons.   are   ear   ore

7. Together we sh_____ a horse

   named Cookie.   are   ear   ore

8. We are learning to c_____ for her.   are   ear   ore

9. We learned that a mother horse is called

   a m_____.   are   ear   ore

10. A horse will r_____ up if she is frightened.   are   ear   ore

Review r-controlled Variant Vowels /âr/*are*; /ôr/*or, ore*; /îr/*ear*

Draw a line to the word that answers each riddle. Then draw a circle around the letters that stand for the vowel sound.

1. It is at the center of an apple.

2. It means to get ready.

3. You can make music on this.

4. It is how you start a letter.

5. It is part of your face.

6. It is like a rabbit.

7. It means "the back of something."

8. It means "not far."

9. A spaceship might be in this.

10. You do this with your ears.

prepare

dear

core

forehead

organ

near

hare

orbit

hear

rear

Review r-controlled Variant Vowels /âr/are; /ôr/or, ore; /îr/ear

Find the word in the box that will finish each sentence. Write it on the line.

forecast	year	before	wore	more
dare	near	ears	scared	care

1. I wanted to skate on the pond

   _____ our school.

2. At last, the _____
   was for cold weather.

3. We didn't _____
   go on the ice until it was very thick.

4. "Wait one _____ day," my Dad said.

5. Finally, on Saturday, we skated _____ lunch.

6. I _____ my new skates.

7. I had a purple hat to keep my _____ warm.

8. Last _____ my little sister was afraid to try.

9. This time she wasn't _____ at all.

10. She didn't seem to _____ about the cold.

Review Variant Vowels /ü/oo, ue, ew

Find the word in the box that goes with each picture. Write it on the line.

moon	clue	statue	igloo	moose	glue
spoon	bluejay	boots	pool	tooth	broom

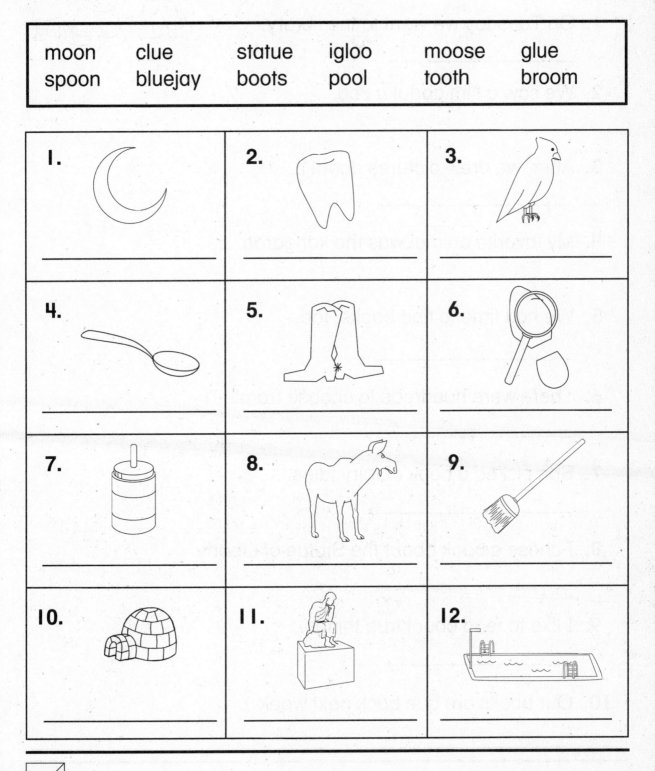

1.

2.

3.

4.

5.

6.

7.

8.

9.

10.

11.

12.

Name _____ Date _____

Review Variant Vowels /ü/*oo, ue, ew*

Draw a circle around the word that has the same
vowel sound as *moon*. Then write it on the line.

1. On Tuesday we went to the library.

   _____

2. We saw a film about a zoo.

   _____

3. After, we drew pictures about it.

   _____

4. My favorite animal was the kangaroo.

   _____

5. We had time to find books, too.

   _____

6. There were hundreds to choose from!

   _____

7. Sue picked a book of fairy tales.

   _____

8. I chose a book about the Statue of Liberty.

   _____

9. I like to read about true things.

   _____

10. Our books are due back next week.

    _____

Review Variant Vowels /ü/*oo, ue, ew*

Draw a circle around the letters that will finish the word in each sentence. Write the letters on the line.

1. Last week my scout tr———p had a cookout.   oo   ue   ew

2. We cooked beef st——— over the fire.   oo   ue   ew

3. The wind bl——— smoke in my eyes.   oo   ue   ew

4. While the f———d cooked, we played soccer.   oo   ue   ew

5. Andrew b———ted the ball for a goal.   oo   ue   ew

6. Sue has ten chickens and one g———se.   oo   ue   ew

7. Her rooster won a bl——— ribbon last year.   oo   ue   ew

8. She keeps the chickens in a c———p.   oo   ue   ew

9. One hen will hatch some eggs s———n.   oo   ue   ew

10. Sue will sell most of them, but she always

    keeps some, t———.   oo   ue   ew

Review Variant Vowels /ü/oo, ue, ew

Draw a line to the word that answers each riddle. Then draw a circle around the letters that stand for the vowel sound.

1. It is twelve o'clock.

2. You eat this.

3. You can swim in this.

4. A detective looks for these.

5. He marries the bride.

6. Animals can be found here.

7. You can weave on this.

8. It makes grass wet.

9. An owl does this.

10. You can sit on it.

food
noon
zoo
loom
pool
clues
stool
groom
dew
hoot

Review /ər/er; /ən/en; /əl/le

Find the name of each picture in the box. Write it on the line.

turtle	paper	farmer	oxen	poster
painter	whistle	stable	eagle	

1. _____

2. _____

3. _____

4. _____

5. _____

6. _____

7. _____

8. _____

9. _____

Review /ər/*er;* /ən/*en;* /əl/*le*

Draw a circle around the letters that will finish the word in each sentence. Write the letters on the line.

1. I will sharp———— my pencil and start a
   new poem.   er   en   le

2. It tells about the flash of lightning and the

   rumb———— of thunder.   er   en   le

3. It tells about gray and silv———— rain.   er   en   le

4. My poem is not scary, so it won't

   fright———— you.   er   en   le

5. Dad says I'm a good writ————.   er   en   le

6. Did I tell you how my brother got in troub————?   er   en   le

7. A woman had a tab———— set up in the
   supermarket.   er   en   le

8. She was giving a free samp———— of
   pepper sauce.   er   en   le

9. My brother squeezed past the count————.   er   en   le

10. How did he happ———— to knock
    everything down?   er   en   le

Review /ər/*er;* /ən/*en;* /əl/*le*

Draw a line to the word that answers each riddle. Then draw a circle around **er, en,** or **le** in the word.

1. He takes your order.

2. This bird is on our money.

3. It carries its house with it.

4. He grows food.

5. It is a place to grow things.

6. Some statues are carved from this.

7. Cowboys herd these.

8. It means the opposite of *loosen.*

farmer

waiter

eagle

turtle

tighten

garden

marble

cattle

Name _____ Date _____

Review /ər/*er;* /ən/*en;* /əl/*le*

Find the word in the box that will finish each sentence. Write it on
the line.

table	better	sharpen	newspaper	taken
brighten	silver	purple	letter	skater

1. I think I'll write a ————————————
   to Grandma.

2. I know that will ———————————
   her day.

3. I'll sit here at the kitchen

   ———————————— to write.

4. I'll send her the picture that was in the

   ————————————.

5. It was ———————————— after the skating race.

6. I came in second and won a———————————— medal.

7. I always ———————————— my skates before a race.

8. I've been working hard to be a faster ————————————.

9. I wore my lucky ———————————— sweater.

10. Next year I hope to do even ————————————.

Name _____ Date _____

Review /ou/ou, ow; /oi/oi, oy

Find the name of each picture in the box. Write it on the line.

toys	mouse	couch	spout	crown	house
boil	flowers	cow	mouth	boy	oil

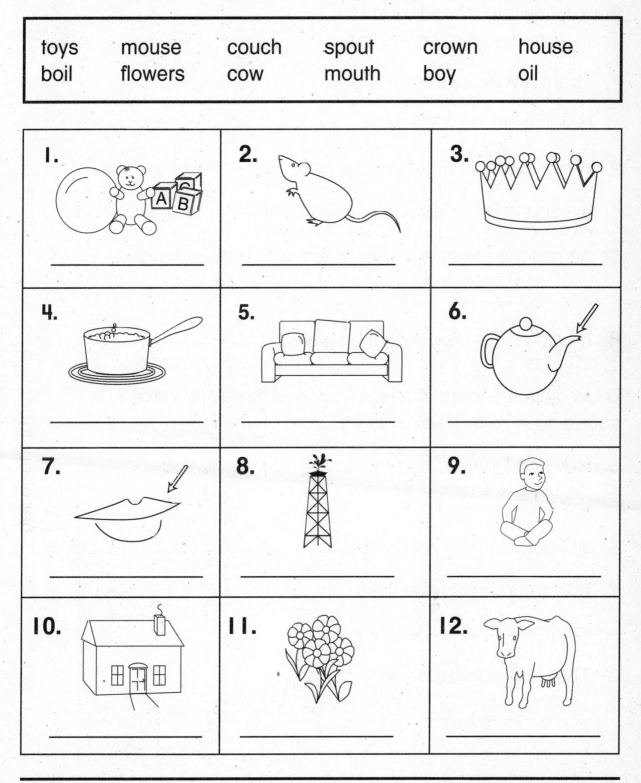

1. _____

2. _____

3. _____

4. _____

5. _____

6. _____

7. _____

8. _____

9. _____

10. _____

11. _____

12. _____

Name_____ Date_____

Review /ou/ou, ow; /oi/oi, oy

Draw a circle around the word that has
the same vowel sound as in *cow*.
Then write the word on the line.

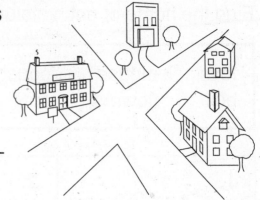

1. There are many interesting

    buildings in my town. _____

2. When the bells ring, you can hear

    the sound for miles. _____

3. Across the street is a small cabin with brown shingles.

    _____

4. It is the oldest house in the state. _____

Draw a circle around the word that has the same vowel
sound as in coin. Then write the word on the line.

5. Roy and I went hiking the day before my birthday.

    _____

6. We both caught poison ivy. _____

7. It is an annoying and itchy

    rash. _____

8. That rash spoiled my birthday party.

    _____

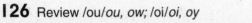

Grade 2   8

Review /ou/*ou*, *ow*; /oi/*oi*, *oy*

Draw a line to the word that answers each riddle. Then draw a circle around the letters that stand for the vowel sound.

1. It is the opposite of quiet.

2. It means "to make wet."

3. You may wear this if you are unhappy.

4. You do this to water to make tea.

5. A royal person could wear this.

6. This is when you lift or pull up.

7. Lemons have this kind of taste.

8. If you are faithful, you are this.

moisten
noisy
sour
crown
boil
loyal
frown
hoist

Name _____ Date _____

Review /ou/*ou*, ow; /oi/*oi*, oy

Find the word in the box that will finish each sentence.
Write it on the line.

flower	trout	brown	outside	broiled
sprout	cloudy	flour	oil	soil

1. My Uncle Jim and I went fishing for _____.

2. We cleaned them and dipped them in egg and _____.

3. Then we poured _____ into the pan.

4. We cooked the fish until they were _____.

5. I like them fried better than _____.

6. I planted some _____ seeds.

7. I started them indoors in moist _____.

8. When they began to _____ I put them in a sunny window.

9. When they are bigger, I will plant them _____ in the garden.

10. It is best to plant them on a _____ day.

Review /ou/; /oi/; /îr/; /âr/; /ôr/; /ü/

Name each picture. Find the missing letters in the box.
Write them on the line.

oo	ew	ue	ear	are	ore
ou	ow	oy	oi		

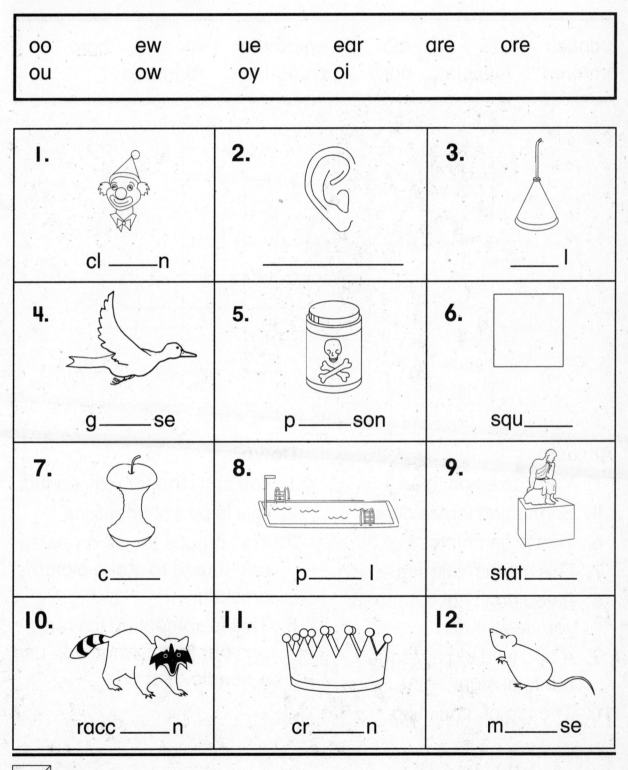

1. cl ____ n

2. _____

3. ____ l

4. g ____ se

5. p ____ son

6. squ ____

7. c ____

8. p ____ l

9. stat ____

10. racc ____ n

11. cr ____ n

12. m ____ se

Name _____ Date _____

Review /ou/; /oi/; / ər/; /âr/; /ôr/; /ü/

Read each clue. Find the answer in the word box. Write the word in the puzzle.

couch	owl	roof	embroider	moist	hare
more	thimble	hoist	computer	forehead	

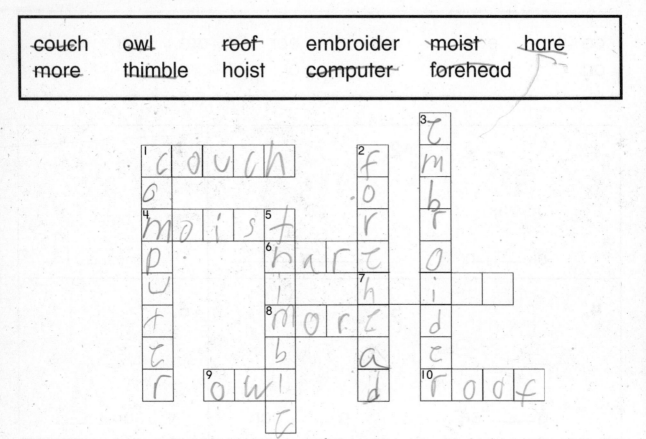

Across

1. You can sit on this.
4. Something that is damp
6. This is an animal.
7. This means to lift something.
8. If you don't have enough, you need this.
9. A bird with big eyes that hunts at night
10. The top of a building

Down

1. You can work or play on this.
2. This is part of your face.
3. This means to use a needle and thread to make pictures on cloth.
5. This is something to wear on your finger when you use a needle.

Review /ou/; /oi/; /ər/; /ən/; /əl/; /ü/

Find the word in the box that will finish each sentence.
Write it on the line.

taken	Joyce	howling	true	shoot
coiled	eagle	pounce	kangaroo	year

1. My Aunt _____ is a photographer.

2. She likes to _____ pictures

   of wild animals.

3. She has _____ some

   wonderful shots.

4. She took one of a mother

   _____ with a baby in her

   pouch.

5. Her photo of a bald _____

   was on the cover of a magazine.

6. She took one of a rattler that was _____ and ready

   to strike.

7. She took another of a tiger ready to _____.

8. I like the one she took of a _____ wolf.

9. Almost every _____ she wins a prize for her work.

10. Her life sounds almost too good to be _____.

Review /ou/; /oi/; /ər/; /ən/; /əl/; /ü/

Draw a line to the word that answers each riddle. Then draw a circle around **er, le,** or **en** in the word.

1. It is something to blow.

2. It is a kind of laugh.

3. It is the room where you cook.

4. A swimmer moves in this.

5. This person moves to music.

6. Do this to a seat belt.

7. You use an iron to get these out.

8. This means "to trip, or fall."

giggle

whistle

water

dancer

kitchen

stumble

wrinkles

fasten

Roy stood up and shone his flashlight into the storeroom. In the glare of the light he saw a family of raccoons!

In the morning Roy's dad called the animal warden. "We'll take them to the woods, far from here," he said. "They won't annoy you anymore."

"I'm proud of you, Roy," said his dad.

For an hour Roy helped his Dad. He went to the rear storeroom. He put things back on the shelves.

Then Roy saw something. A few flour bags were ripped open. Flour had spilled out.

But the prowler had left a clue!

Fold the right side back on the long center line. Then fold the top half under the bottom half on the short center line. Cut open the tops of the pages.

Roy Catches a Prowler

As soon as Roy went into the kitchen he knew something was wrong.

"Dad!" he asked. "Why aren't you in the store?"

"I'm afraid we have trouble," Mr. Spear answered. "Someone broke into the store last night."

"Hmm," said Roy. "That's odd."

Dad said, "The police told me there have been other reports of prowlers. They will have a car drive by the store every hour."

"I wonder how the prowler got in," said Roy.

"Maybe I forgot to fasten the lock," said Dad.

Just then he heard a noise from the storeroom. Roy didn't dare move. Something jiggled the window! Roy felt a trickle of fear down his spine.

Roy Catches a Prowler McGraw-Hill Scho

"I think I know who our prowler is," thought Roy.

That night, Roy waited until his parents were asleep. Then he got his scout flashlight. He went downstairs to the store. He crouched behind the counter and waited.

An hour went by.

"Maybe this is foolish," thought Roy.

"Maybe the prowler is dangerous." thought Roy. He began to feel a little scared.

Roy went downstairs to the store. Broken bottles and ripped packages were everywhere.

"Wow!" said Roy. "Whoever it was, trashed the place."

"Yes," his dad said. "A lot of the food is spoiled. I'm afraid we are closed today."

After school Roy hurried to the store. His Dad was still cleaning up.

"It has taken me all day to straighten up," he grumbled.

"But I guess they were frightened off. They left before they found any money."

Review Digraphs

Find the name of each picture in the box. Write it on the line.

chipmunk	graph	pheasant	torch	trophy
patch	wrench	dolphin	bench	

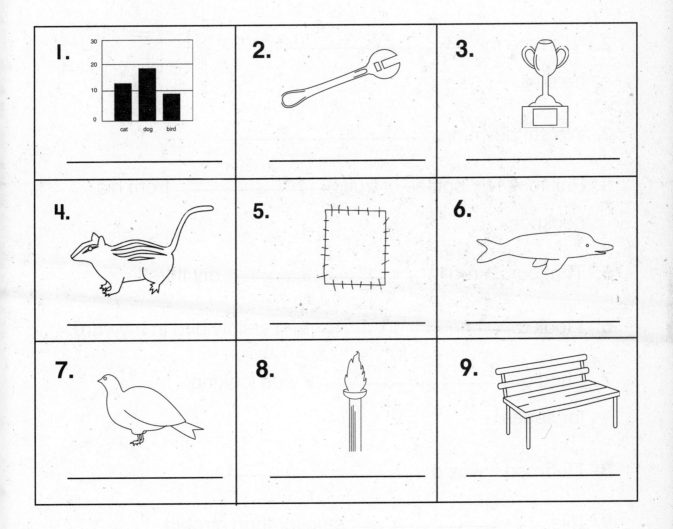

1. _____

2. _____

3. _____

4. _____

5. _____

6. _____

7. _____

8. _____

9. _____

Name _____ Date _____

Review Digraphs

Find the word in the box that will finish each sentence. Write it on the line.

lunch	quenched	such	much	photo
bench	hunch	watch	punch	finch

1. As we walked through the park, Phil looked at his ———————.

2. "It's time for ———————,"
   he said.

3. We sat down on a ———————.

4. Phil took two bottles of fruit ——————— from his backpack.

5. That punch really ——————— my thirst!

6. I took a ——————— of a yellow bird in my yard.

7. I had a ——————— it was looking for seeds.

8. I learned it was a ———————.

9. It is ——————— smaller than a robin.

10. It is ——————— a cheery sight!

Review Digraphs

Read each clue. Find the answer in the word box. Write
the word in the puzzle.

chin	rush	rich	photographer	pitcher
graph	hitch	bunch	porch	wrench

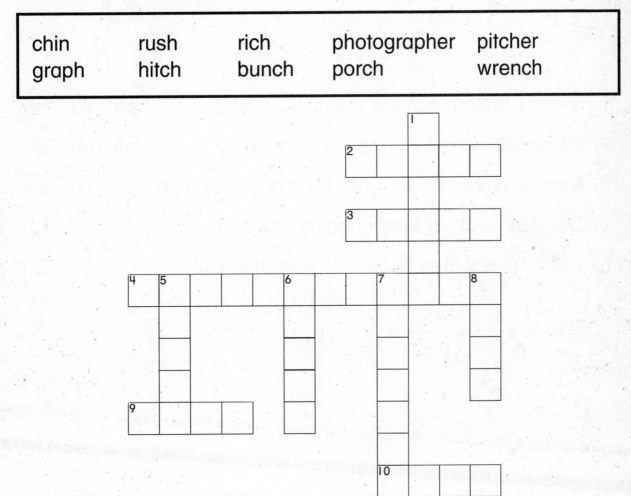

Across

2. A house might have this.
3. Grapes come in this.
4. This person takes photos.
9. The part of your face that is under your mouth.
10. If you move quickly, you do this.

Down

1. This is a tool a plumber uses.
5. You do this to a trailer.
6. It is a way to show numbers.
7. A player on a baseball team
8. Someone who has lots of money is this.

Review Digraphs

Draw a circle around the letters that will finish the
word in each sentence. Write the letters on the
line.

1. My little brother can say the al——abet .   ph   ch   tch

2. He says it every ——ance he gets.   ph   ch   tch

3. Mom says it is a ——ase he is going through.   ph   ch   tch

4. Dad just ——uckles when he starts.   ph   ch   tch

5. I wish he would swi—— to something new.   ph   ch   tch

6. Did you watch ——annel 5 on TV last night?   ph   ch   tch

7. There was a show about dol——ins.   ph   ch   tch

8. They were playing ca—— with a ball.   ph   ch   tch

9. Do you think dolphins are smarter than

   ——imps?   ph   ch   tch

10. Which would you ——oose to learn more

    about?   ph   ch   tch

Review Long *e*; Long *i*

Find the name of each picture in the box. Write it on the line.

feet	cheek	night	light	beach	sleeve
hydrant	peas	chimney	fly	icicle	teapot

1. _____

2. _____

3. _____

4. _____

5. _____

6. _____

7. _____

8. _____

9. _____

10. _____

11. _____

12. _____

Review Long *e*; Long *i*

Draw a circle around the word that has the same vowel sound as in *tree*. Write the letters that stand for the sound.

1. The princess lay down to sleep. _____

2. Someone had put a pea under the mattress. _____

3. "Good grief!" the princess said. _____

4. "I can't believe how awful this bed is." _____

5. That's how they knew she was a real princess. _____

Draw a circle around the word that has the same vowel sound as in *fly*. Write the letters that stand for the sound.

6. The princess was locked in a high tower. _____

7. A brave knight rode up to the castle. _____

8. "Don't cry," he said. _____

9. "I am not the type," said the princess. _____

10. "But thank you for saving me from my plight." _____

Review Long *e*; Long *i*

Find the word in the box that will finish each sentence.
Write it on the line.

relief	tea	feel	street
sleep	night	chief	read

1. Did you hear the fire alarm last

_____?

2. It was a _____ when it
stopped.

3. The fire was across the

_____ from me.

4. The fire _____ got there first.

5. Her Mom didn't wake her, but let her _____ late.

6. She let her stay in bed and _____ , too.

7. Her Mom made her drink _____ with lemon.

8. Soon she said, "I _____ much better."

Review Long *e*; Long *i*

Draw a line to the word that answers each riddle. Then draw a circle around the letters that stand for the vowel sound.

1. It is a way to cook potatoes.

2. This is a big pile.

3. He was a fighter in the past.

4. This is a long, deep sound.

5. If there is no war, we have this.

6. Something that is special

7. This means "power."

8. This is something you might ask.

heap

fry

knight

sigh

why

treat

peace

might

Name _____ Date _____

Review Long *a*; Long *o*

Draw a circle around each word that has the same vowel sound as the name of the picture.

1. hope / tot / slope / slow	**2.** cope / soap / call / foam	**3.** top / bone / boat / flow
toad	coal	blow
4. rake / pain / pail / ran	**5.** hail / snail / hat / stay	**6.** got / throw / go / slow
chain	hay	pillow
7. gain / boat / grow / soap	**8.** train / trip / pay / hail	**9.** coat / mat / hope / slow
goat	tray	boat

Review Long *a*; Long *o*

Find the word in the box that will finish each sentence. Write it on the line.

roast	know	train	grain
rain	sail	grow	goal

1. Would you like to _____ on a boat?

2. Would you like to travel by _____?

3. My _____ is to travel around the world.

4. I _____ that I will do it one day.

5. Many farmers _____ corn.

6. Corn, like wheat, is a kind of

   _____.

7. Corn needs lots of

   _____ to grow well.

8. I love to _____ and eat corn on the cob.

Review Long *a*; Long *o*

Draw a circle around the word that has the same vowel sound as *snail*. Then write the word on the line.

1. Jill bought some clay at the store. _____

2. She paid for it with her own money. _____

3. She is making animals for a display. _____

4. She plans to paint them. _____

5. Should she spray them or use a brush? _____

Draw a line under the word that has the same vowel sound as in *boat*. Then write the word on the line.

6. Tim was delighted that it snowed. _____

7. His dad cleared the walk with the blower. _____

8. But the road in front of their house was very bad. _____

9. The cars slowed to a crawl. _____

10. One car got stuck and had to be towed. _____

Review Long *a*; Long *o*

Draw a line to the word that answers each riddle. Then draw a circle around the letters that stand for the vowel sound.

1. You wash with this.

2. You can color with this.

3. Spilled grape juice will do this.

4. A water hose can do this.

5. You can take a ride in this.

6. Dirty water goes down this.

7. You may see this when you pour soda.

8. This is a baby horse.

9. This can be seen by many.

10. It looks like a frog.

stain

soap

spray

crayon

show

toad

train

foam

foal

drain

20

Review Soft *c*; Soft *g*

Find the name of each picture in the box. Write it on the line.

ice cream	badge	gerbil	bridge	face	giraffe
hinge	cent	lace	sponge	judge	cage

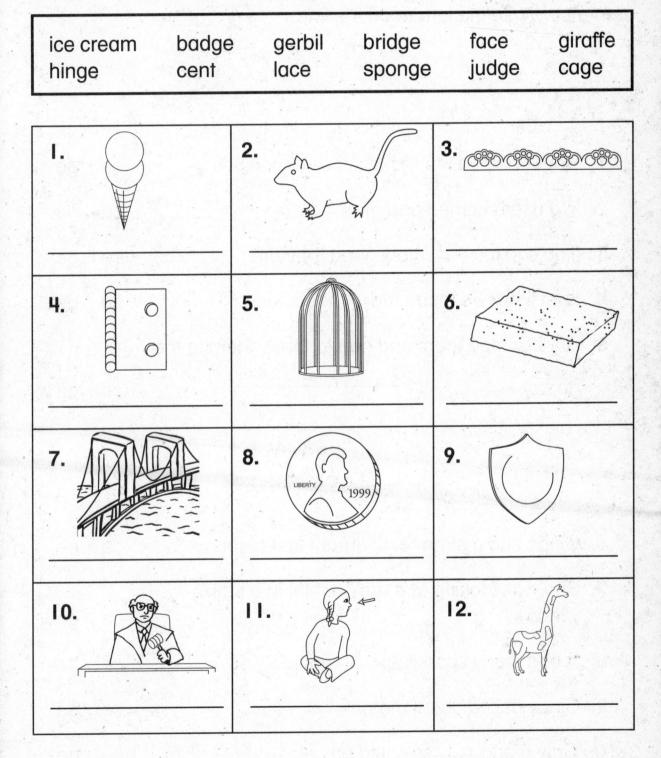

1. _____

2. _____

3. _____

4. _____

5. _____

6. _____

7. _____

8. _____

9. _____

10. _____

11. _____

12. _____

Review Soft *c*; Soft *g*

Draw a circle around the letters that will finish the word in each sentence. Write the letters on the line.

1. Roger helped me make spi——— cookies.   ce   ge

2. We used nutmeg and gin———r.   ce   ge

3. You can jud——— how good they are.   ce   ge

4. Last time, we made fud——— cookies.   ce   ge

5. But I burned them and had to throw them in the

   garba———.   ce   ge

6. Cindy had a stran——— dream last night.   ce   ge

7. She was looking at a bra———let in a store
   window.   ce   ge

8. It had many sparkling ———ms in it.   ce   ge

9. Cindy asked about the pri———.   ce   ge

10. Only a prin———ss could buy it!   ce   ge

Review Soft *c*; Soft *g*

Draw a line to the word that answers each riddle.
Then draw a circle around **ce** or **ge**.

1. You can keep this in a cage.

2. This means two times.

3. A necklace could have these.

4. This tells how old you are.

5. This is a promise.

6. You can use this in the bathtub.

7. This is sweet to eat.

8. These people watch a play.

gerbil

twice

sponge

gems

fudge

age

audience

pledge

Review Soft *c*; Soft *g*

Find the word in the box that will finish each sentence. Write it on the line.

danger	hinge	rummage	glanced	ice
package	pounce	cellar	face	large

1. What is making that noise in the

   _____?

2. Is there any _____?

3. Is it something that could

   _____ on me?

4. I'm not afraid. I can _____ it.

5. Look! It is just a rusty _____.

6. Jill _____ at the table.

7. There was a _____
   there.

8. "What is that _____ box?" she asked.

9. "Something I got at the _____ sale,"
   Mom said.

10. "It's an _____ cream maker."

Review Long Vowels

Draw a circle around each word that has the same vowel sound as the name of the picture.

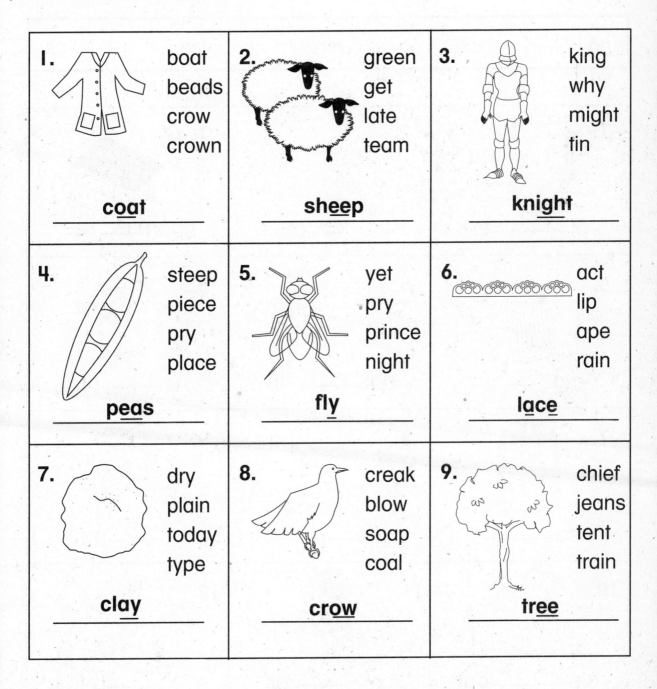

1.
boat
beads
crow
crown

coat

2.
green
get
late
team

sheep

3.
king
why
might
tin

knight

4.
steep
piece
pry
place

peas

5.
yet
pry
prince
night

fly

6.
act
lip
ape
rain

lace

7.
dry
plain
today
type

clay

8.
creak
blow
soap
coal

crow

9.
chief
jeans
tent
train

tree

Name _____ Date _____

Review Digraphs *ph, ch, tch*; Soft *c*; Soft *g*

Name each picture. Find the missing letters in the box. Write them on the line.

ph	ch	tch	ce	ge

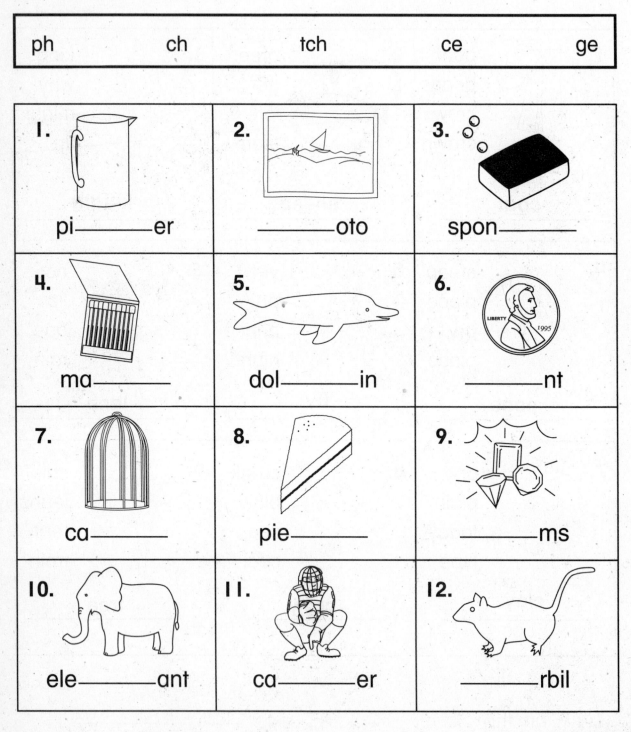

1.
pi____er

2.
____oto

3.
spon____

4.
ma____

5.
dol____in

6.
____nt

7.
ca____

8.
pie____

9.
____ms

10.
ele____ant

11.
ca____er

12.
____rbil

Review Long Vowels; Digraphs *ph, ch, tch*; Soft *c*: Soft *g*

Find the word in the box that will finish each sentence. Write it on the line.

fudge	claims	wedge	boasted	stretch
sighed	phone	outgrown	greedy	tight

1. Madge reached for another piece of _____ cake.

2. "Don't be _____ ," her brother said.

3. "You already had a big _____ of cake before."

4. Just then the _____ rang.

5. "Mom says to save the cake for supper,"

   Madge _____ .

6. Phil _____ he has grown two inches this year.

7. His pants are too _____ .

8. He has _____ his shirt, too.

9. His clothes won't _____ to fit him.

10. "I am the tallest in my class," he _____ .

Review Long Vowels; Digraphs *ph, ch, tch*; Soft *c*: Soft *g*

Read each clue. Find the answer in the word box. Write the word in the puzzle.

scratch	display	stage	loan	high	float
grain	stitch	leaf	elephant	night	

Down

1. You do this with a needle.
3. This is a large animal.
4. Oats and corn are two kinds of this.
6. This is when the sun does not shine.
9. It is something a plant has.

Across

2. This is where actors work.
5. This means to let someone use something.
7. A cat can do this.
8. This means to put something where people can see it.
10. This means "not low."
11. Wood can do this.

"Wow!" said Madge.

"Cool," said Gerry and Phil.

"It has real feeling," said Miss Dean.

Kay just smiled.

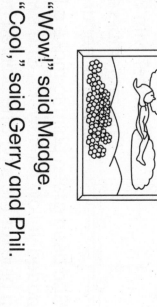

Meantime, Miss Dean praised Phil's icebergs and his gray sky. She praised Gerry's sea creature and Madge's geranium.

When she reached Kay's desk, she asked, "Are you having trouble?"

"Yes," sighed Kay. "I can't paint anything beautiful."

Fold the right side back on the long center line. Then fold the top half under the bottom half on the short center line. Cut open the tops of the pages.

"You should all paint something for the show," Miss Dean said.

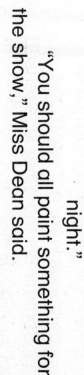

The Art Show

"We are having an art show," said Miss Dean. "It will take place next Friday night."

Kay tried. She started three paintings but threw them all away. She took a new sheet of paper. She stared at it.

Madge leaned over. "Let me see your picture," she said.

Kay wished she could switch seats.

"Paintings don't have to be beautiful. They don't need to look like a photograph. Just paint what you feel," said Miss Dean. "Let the colors flow."

That night Kay had a dream. She was floating in a blue sky with pink clouds. She saw a green field with yellow flowers below her. She felt free and peaceful.

The next day Kay tried again. She wet her paper with water. She remembered the feeling of her dream.

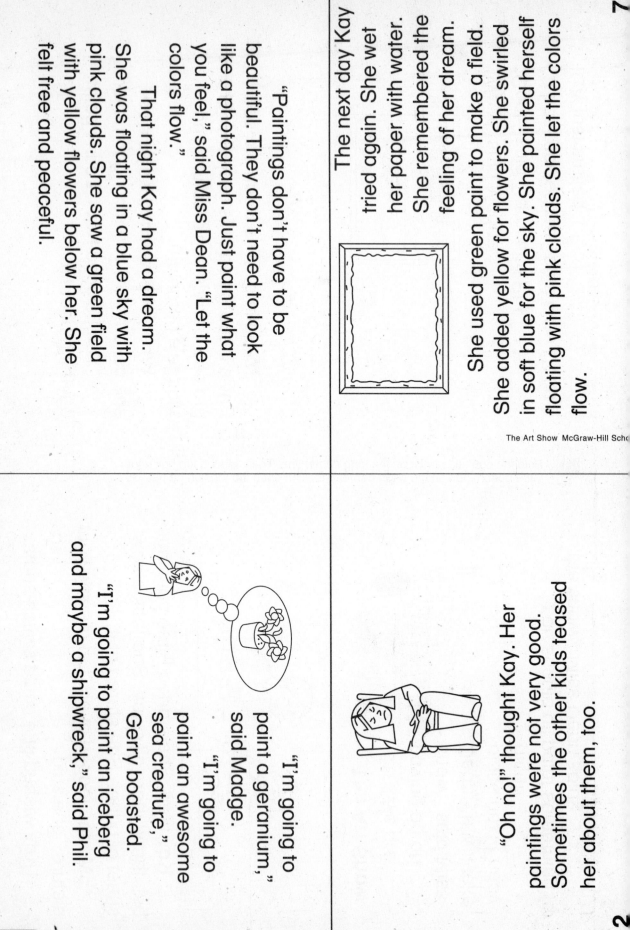

She used green paint to make a field. She added yellow for flowers. She swirled in soft blue for the sky. She painted herself floating with pink clouds. She let the colors flow.

The Art Show McGraw-Hill Scho

"I'm going to paint a geranium," said Madge.

"I'm going to paint an awesome sea creature," Gerry boasted.

"I'm going to paint an iceberg and maybe a shipwreck," said Phil.

"Oh no!" thought Kay. Her paintings were not very good. Sometimes the other kids teased her about them, too.